A
JAIME
DE ANGULO
READER

A
JAIME
DE ANGULO
READER

Edited &
with an Introduction
by Bob Callahan

Turtle Island, Berkeley 1979

Contents

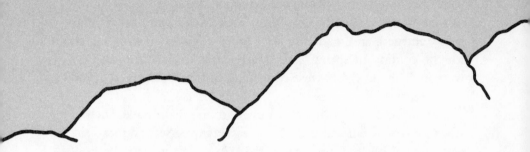

On Jaime de Angulo

Winter comes early to Alturas. The snow begins to fall in early October, and the long arctic winters stay until the last days of March. The Pit River Indians have lived on that barren, forbidding plateau in Northeastern California for thousands of years. The Snow People. That's what the Modoc call them. In the old days, with the first flakes of winter, the Indians would climb down through the smoke hole into the winter lodges.

Inside the lodge, dug into the ground, the roof covered with earth, it was warm even with a small fire. "Yet, you have to be Indian," Jaime de Angulo writes, "to stand the crowding, the lack of privacy, the eternal squabbling of babies. And after a few

x   A de Angulo Reader

months of occupancy the vermin were terrible. Once in a while someone would take out the old litter and bring in a fresh supply of pine boughs. But the fleas, lice, cockroaches, and other bugs soon returned, and made life once more a misery. People sighed for the coming of spring, and quarreled as to what month they were in. The old chiefs were consulted, but they disagreed." And so winter passed.

In those days the Pit River Indians didn't really have much of what we would call 'culture.' Their baskets were second rate—the patterns too blurred, too crude. No skin painting, nothing at all unusual about their dress. Even their dancing was inferior: stiff, awkward, too rapid. "Singing was about the only form of art developed by those Indians," de Angulo writes. Singing, and old-time stories.

Jaime de Angulo bought a cattle ranch in Alturas in 1913. Dr. Jaime de Angulo. The son of a Spanish Don, de Angulo came to America at the age of eighteen, and worked his way out west as a cowboy, taking odd jobs on ranches in Wyoming and Colorado. He arrived in San Francisco just in time for the earthquake of '06. In San Francisco he began to study medicine at the former Cooper Medical College—Cooper then to Johns Hopkins where he received his first medical degree in 1912. The next year de Angulo became a partner in the ranch, and met the Pit River people for the first time. His introduction was cut short however by the outbreak of the First World War. De Angulo volunteered for service, and before long he was sent to Ann Arbor to attend an early course on psychiatry for army doctors. He graduated, then stayed on as instructor at the school for the remainder of the war.

Back at the ranch a few months later, de Angulo decided to drive a herd of horses down from the plateau through the long, five hundred mile central valley to new homestead land in the Big Sur. He was living on the new land in the summer of 1919, when two college professors, Alfred Kroeber and Paul Radin, rented a cabin nearby. During the next few months the three men became close friends, and by the end of the summer de Angulo had accepted Kroeber's invitation to join him at the University the next year. So in 1920, Jaime de Angulo left cattle ranching for a while and taught his first two courses in Berkeley, one in Jungian Psychiatry, the other on the Mind of Primitive Man. De Angulo helped inaugurate the 'Golden Age of American Anthropology' at Cal. Kroeber and Radin were already in residence when he arrived; Robert Lowie, Carl O. Sauer, and briefly, Edward Sapir would also join the staff by the end of the decade.

Jaime de Angulo's presence alone, one suspects, would have been enough. His wonderful ear for language quickened the environment. In the company of these men, he expanded his interests, seventeen new languages during the next fifteen years. Chatino, Chichimeco, Chinanteco, Chocho, Chontal, Mazateco, Mixe, Teqistlatec and Zapotex proper. The Indians of Mexico. Karok, Klamath, Modoc, Miwok, Paiute, Pomo, Shastan and Achumawi. The Indians of Northern California. He even managed to translate Lao-Tsu with the help of only a small pocket dictionary. But de Angulo began with Achumawi, the spoken language of his former Pit River friends. In 1921, he returned once more to Alturas, this time to record the grammar and the literature of his chosen tribe.

"Real Primitive People," he would write, "not like those 'cultured' Indians of the Southwest . . . real stone age men . . . my Indians in Overalls." Season after season he camped with Old Jack Folsom and Lena in the sagebrush on the Plateau. His eye caught the detail of gambling games and healing rites, and his ear, always his ear, picked up the short, clipped cadences of the Pit River tongue. He never lost his fascination with that language. In de Angulo's later novels, David Olmsted writes, the Indians continue to speak "in sentences which are undeniably and perfectly grammatical Achumawi!"

In winter camp de Angulo began to translate the *Dilasani qi*, the old-time stories of the Pit River People, the spirit history of

the tribe. In the beginning was the Word . . . the stories, he felt,
dated back into the furthest reaches of the stone age, were more
ancient than myth. And the Word was with God . . . in these
stories he felt he had found one of man's earliest attempts to make
articulate the movement of the Spirit. And the Word was God . . .
"The symbolism in these stories is so crude and so little disguised
that it can't really be considered symbolism at all. In this early,
primitive stage of civilization, ideas are still immanent in objects,
and have not yet been separated either through identification or
projection. In these stories we find the Tinihowi—the primitive
religious spirit—reflected throughout . . . and yet, the reader
might ask, if the Pit River Indians have no religious ceremonies,
no priesthood, no ritual of any kind, and not the slightest approach to any conception of Godhead, how can one speak of their
having any spiritual or religious values? I grant that it may sound
somewhat paradoxical, but I must answer on the contrary, the life
of these Indians is nothing but a continuous religous experience
. . . The spirit of wonder, the *recognition of life as power*, as a mysterious, ubiquitous, concentrated form of nonmaterial energy, of
something loose about the world and contained in a more or less
condensed degree by every object—this is the credo of the Pit
River Indians. Of course they would not put it precisely this way.
The phraseology is mine, but it is not far from their own." Jaime
de Angulo had rediscovered the Logos. Formed and transformed
by a hundred Sierra mountain Homers, sung back & forth in
these hills for thousands of years, the *Dilasani qi* were born that
first morning. *Dilasani qi*. The Origin.

De Angulo left academic life in 1934. In the grasp of an endless series of personal tragedies, he turned more and more to
poetry and literature. In the late 40's, he began to rewrite his early
Northern California Indian texts to the delight of his children.
The project grew, and after considerable revision, out popped the
book called *Indian Tales*. In 1949, he read the final text to an astonished audience over radio station KPFA in Berkeley. A year
later he was dead.

In later life, de Angulo had become something of a legend here in Northern California, both a legend and a mystery. A tragic, dark figure, some would say, the darkness of a northcoast Poe. No, old friends replied, he was just 'wandering'. "I want to speak now," he wrote that first spring, "of a certain curious phenomenon found among the Pit River Indians. The Indians refer to it in English as 'wandering'. They say of a certain man, 'He is wandering', or 'He has started to wander'. It would seem that under certain conditions of mental stress an individual finds life in his accustomed surroundings impossible to bear. Such a man starts to wander. He goes about the country, traveling aimlessly. He will stop here and there at the camps of friends or relations, moving on, never stopping at any place any longer than a few days. He will not make any outward show of grief, sorrow or worry. In fact, he will speak of what is on his mind to no one, but anyone can see that he is not all right. He is morose, uncommunicative. Without any warning, he will get up and go. People will probably say of such a man: 'He has lost his shadow. He ought to get to a doctor to get it back for him before it is too late.'

"The Wanderer, man or woman, shuns camps and villages, remains in wild, lonely places, on the tops of mountains, in the bottoms of canyons. Whenever anyone approaches, he runs away, throws sticks and rocks at his friends and relatives. They will spy on him, waiting for his condition to improve. They find him performing antics of behavior, running and jumping, with shouts and songs, and breaking branches, hurling rocks at trees.

"Wandering is something that may unfortunately befall any man or woman, and it can take many, many forms. It may end up in complete loss of soul, and lingering death. When an Indian becomes convinced that he has lost his shadow, he will let himself die out of sheer hopelessness. Or it may result in temporary madness. The Indian never courts pain. It would never enter his head to imagine that by making himself miserable and pitiful in the eyes of the Powers he might gain their sympathy and aid. This is not his conception at all. To him, the mysterious powers, the

Tinihowis (we might call them genii), are whimsical spirits living in the woods and entirely indifferent to the affairs of the Pit River Valley. In order to gain their friendship, in order to approach them without scaring them away, it is necessary to become wild oneself, it is necessary to lose one's own humanhood and become as wild as possible, as crazy as possible. Haunt lonely, desolate places. Act like a madman, throw rocks about, yell and dance like a maniac, run away when anybody comes. Climb awful mountains, climb down the rim of crater lakes, jump into the silent cold water, spend all night there. Of course, one suffers cold and hunger in such an experience, but it is only a necessary and inevitable accompaniment of getting wild. When you have become quite wild, then perhaps some of the wild things will come to take a look at you, and one of them may perhaps take a fancy to you, not because you are suffering and cold, but simply because he happens to like your looks. When this happens, the wandering is over, and the Indian becomes a shaman."

All white men are wanderers, the old people say; at the end de Angulo was trying to get home.

Bob Callahan
San Francisco
Spring 1973

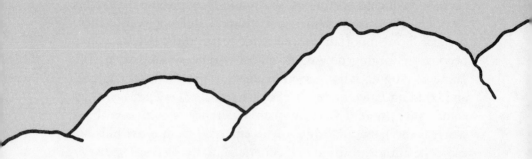

Notes for a New Edition

In reconsidering my introduction, first written over five years ago to announce the Turtle Island hardcover edition of de Angulo's selected works, I now find still another important de Angulo geographic center missing from the text, and this would be the isolate and rather wild La Costa del Sur.

Berkeley, the Pit River country around Alturas, and the lonely days on Partington Ridge—these three places provided a home, as nearly as any place could, for this extraordinary Basqueman whose roots, he would often claim, went all the way back to Biscay Bay. Cro-Magnon Jaime de Angulo.

Yes, Big Sur is hardly mentioned at all in that earlier

introduction—partially because Henry Miller has already drawn such a convincing portrait of de Angulo during those days in his own *The Devil in Paradise*—but more, I did not realize then, perhaps, how important those hermit years on the lone coast had become in forging de Angulo's final mature writing style. The Jaime de Angulo who arrived in Big Sur was the crack linguist, and budding Lawrentian novelist who wrote *Don Bartolomeo*—in some ways more Lawrence than Lawrence would ever be—whereas the Jaime de Angulo who emerged from those hills became the author of those two American masterpieces, *The Lariat* and *Indians in Overalls*.

It seems all too much like King Lear.

And, of course, our own Press has grown up around the publication of these individual de Angulo works. We live, write and publish in Berkeley, in a house that Nancy & Jaime de Angulo once built, and daughter Guiomar, Oriole-Girl of the famous *Indian Tales*, our friend Gui, is now our next-door neighbor. And Clifford Burke, who printed those beautiful first editions, is beginning a new business up near Seattle, after years of some "wandering" on his own. For many among my generation, the road from the late Sixties to here has been long, twisted and at times totally mystifying.

I welcome, therefore, the opportunity for this new *de Angulo Reader*. Jaime de Angulo was, as his friend Carl Sauer once said, "one of the rarest spirits of his time," and became, according to William Carlos Williams, "one of America's most wonderful writers." Perhaps now, with the publication of this paperback volume, many more Americans will come to appreciate the charm and the genius of this truly remarkable man.

Bob Callahan
Berkeley
Spring, 1978

I: EARLY WORKS

Five Thousand Years

Five Thousand Years is very early de Angulo, and represents no more than a sketch of the author's final writing style. I think of it as a blueprint, really, for so many of the books still to come. *Five Thousand Years* was written on the destruction of Shell Mound Park back in the early Twenties. Today a paint factory sits on the site of these ancient mounds.

Five Thousand Years

On the shore of the Bay, across from San Francisco, where the Saklan once lived and hunted and fished and dug clams and sat around their campfires, they are digging away one of the big shell mounds with a steam shovel.

An acre of shells twenty feet deep.

It is close to the railroad tracks. Trains rumble by. Factory whistles blow. Chimney stacks all around. Valuable land. The steam shovel crunches into the shell mound.

Across the bay, Tamalpais, always beautiful. Other tribes of the Miwok had their campfires in those hills.

Sometimes, the steam shovel crunches into a skeleton to the

delight of the anthropologists who come here every day to watch for discoveries. You don't often get such an opportunity. They recover every valuable bit from the tons of rubbish. Some little balls of stone with a hole drilled through—what were the thoughts of the woman who wore them as a necklace? What was she like? Young sturdy mother stirring the acorn mush, or withered, half-blind old witch muttering by the fire? And this broken fishhook of soapstone. Perhaps a young boy, with his ears yet unpierced, threw it away crossly; he had sat so long by the fire, evening after evening, grinding it into shape. Or perhaps it was a full-fledged hunter, accustomed to the hardships, who lost it.

Spearheads, bone awls, an obsidian knife traded from the north—on the whole, not much. There was not much of a culture in the Neolithic Age.

An acre of campfire refuse twenty feet deep.

They say it represents five thousand years.

Five thousand years without any advance in material culture. Five thousand years of living on the shores of the Bay, always the same—hunting, digging for clams, reciting the old tales around the campfires; the tale of Yayali the Giant; the tale of how "He Who Walks Alone" made the world and Coyote helped him; the tale of how the fire was stolen from the people who had it.

It was Lizard who first saw the smoke, and he said: "Smoking below, smoking below, smoking below, smoking below. My grandmother starts a fire to cook acorns. It is very lonely." And they sent Flute-player, the Mouse, to get the fire. He took with him four flutes. He put the people to sleep with his music and he stole their fire. He filled his flutes with coals and brought them back to his people.

And another time they stole the Sun. It was Coyote who stole the Sun. He discovered the Sun on one of these trips. He wondered how he could get it. He changed himself into a broken stick and lay down on the path. The chief came along. He took the stick home for his fire. He was getting sleepy. He kept poking the stick back into the fire. Always, it jumped out. When the chief fell asleep, the stick changed back into Coyote. He ran away with the Sun and brought him back to his own people in the dark land.

They sit around the fire telling the old stories. They hunt and gather acorns. They dig for roots. They sit in the sun for hours, chipping flint knives. They wander in lonely places and talk to the spirits. For five thousand years, the same; they watch the Sun in the daytime and the Moon at night. They call them by the same name. For five thousand years, the same; they sit around the fire, they look into the fire, wondering, dreaming.

In fifty years they have all gone.

The trains rumble by. Eastbound trains. Through the desert where the warlike Mohaves roved. Up through higher lands to the mesas of the Southwest; through the country of the wild Apaches, of the taciturn Navajos; through the land where the Pueblos live in their villages.

They dance in the Pueblos. Elaborate dances. The acme of ritual. In the kivas, underground, the secret societies perform their long rites. The Sun beats fiercely in this droughty land. We must raise Corn or starve. The land is frozen hard. Oh Sun, Father, beat hard upon the land. Warm our Mother. We dance upon the Earth. We dance hard to the beat of the drum. We wave the sacred Corn. Scatter the pollen. Come down, Rain. Rain maker, hear us. Fire for the Sun. Water for the Earth. We offer food to our parents. Breed, O Sun, O Earth. Breed the world for your children.

Taos, the highest of the Pueblos, sleeping at the foot of a mountain. Taos proudly secret. Wake up in the Pueblo, make ready for the vernal equinox. Our Father is waking up out of his long sleep. Make ready, men and women. The whole people will move up to the mountain for three days. The summer people and the winter people. They will sing all night till their voices crack. It is now time for the winter people to hand the Sun over to the summer people. They will take care of him now.

They dance sullenly in the Pueblos, for the whites are watching.

The whites have forbidden the dances.

The whites understand nothing. They think the Sun is just a shining plate. They are cold and cruel. They kill everything they can. They think only with their heads. They have lost their hearts. That is why all the animals are hiding in the mountains. It is because they don't like the smell of the whites.

The Sun and the Moon and the Stars and the Earth are working for us. You can't pay them with money. Only with your heart. That's what we Indians do. We do it for ourselves, and for the whole world, and for you, too. Why do you want to stop us?

For five thousand years they looked into the fire. Then they knew.

The trains rumble by with fire in their engines. The factories whir incessantly with fire in their engines. The white men run about, crazy. They have lost something.

The Symbol is dead like a shiny plate. Knowledge is like life. It must forever die to be reborn.

Don Bartolomeo

Don Bartolomeo is de Angulo's first novel, very much a first novel, and was written in the Big Sur during the winter of 1922, immediately after de Angulo's separation from his first wife, the late Cary Fink. Fink had fallen in love with a young Jungian analyst by the name of Joseph Baynes, and had gone off with Baynes to join the Jungian community in Switzerland. In later years a remarried Cary F. Baynes would be employed to provide translation for the first English edition of Richard Wilhelm's *I Ching*.

In any event the winter of 1922 was a difficult one for Jaime de Angulo, and his difficulty was compounded by banishment from the D. H. Lawrence circle in Taos where he had been a more or less active and regular member. Along with the writings of Lawrence, and the young Haniel Long, de Angulo's first essays had begun to appear in Spud Johnson's magazine *Laughing Horse,* but when Lawrence actually arrived in Taos a falling out of some order occurred. Some say Lawrence could not tolerate another 'white Indian' around to challenge his own perceptions into the 'blood consciousness' of Native American culture; others say it was a simple matter of sexual jealousy—although the question of just who was jealous of whom remains an open question, and somewhat in doubt.

In the winter of 1922, therefore, ostracized from Taos, and with his first wife gone off to Switzerland, Jaime de Angulo returned to Big Sur to attempt a 'shimmering,' mildly incestuous little pot-boiler of a novel all on his own.

One final irony: it was Carl Jung who put de Angulo in touch with the editor of the *Weekly Independent* back in Boston where *Don Bartolomeo* was first published, in four issues, back in 1925.

Don Bartolomeo

I am the last Indian of my tribe, the last of the Sureños. There are
some Indians around Carmel, but I don't understand their language. They are another people altogether, and they will soon go,
too. All the Indians are bound to die, now that you people have
killed our protectors, the eagles, the lions, the bears . . . the masters of the mountains, the señores of the brush.

I am a half-breed myself, at that. My father was a brother of
Don Bartolomeo who owned this ranch and all the land around
here. That was a very long time ago, before you white people
came, when this country belonged to the Spaniards. I am very,
very old, you know. I don't know how old I am. I can't read.

I never saw my father. My mother said he had laughing eyes, and nobody could help doing what he wanted. His eyes were blue. You see how my eyes are almost blue, also.

He arrived one evening at the ranch on a very tired horse when nobody was expecting him. My mother told me all that. She was a young girl, then. She worked in the house. Don Bartolomeo was very much annoyed. He said to his brother, "You look all tired out and your horse, also; when did you leave Monterey?"

"This morning, quite early."

"This morning? This morning!" (You see it's a good fifty miles from here to Monterey, and in those days there was no road after the mission at Carmel—just a rough trail, up and down, all the way, up and down.) "You came all the way from town in one day? Another *calaverada,* eh?"

"Yes, I killed a man."

"Whom did you kill?"

"Don Braulio."

"Don Braulio! But—but why?"

My father then looked at his sister-in-law who had come in and was standing there with my mother. He looked at her and he smiled. "How can you stand a man who asks so many questions!" he said, and then he turned to his brother again. "Well," he said, and seemed to hesitate a little, "well, he came in too early!"

"Ah," said Don Bartolomeo, "I ought to have guessed. Brother, brother, women will yet lead you to the garrote, you'll see."

"Well, they are worth it, aren't they?" said my father, turning to where the two women stood, and Doña Mercedes giggled. This made Don Bartolomeo furious. He turned to her and asked her why she laughed. She became silent immediately and murmured, *"Nada, nada, dispensame."* Doña Mercedes was very beautiful, my mother told me, and very white. She did not come from Monterey. She came from another place, very far, very far, so she said. And then she would dream and sing, my mother said. My mother worked in the house, you know.

Don Bartolomeo was very much annoyed. He paced up and down the room, mumbling and looking angrily at his brother, who had seated himself in front of the fire and was smoking. At last he stopped: "I have to protect you again because you are my blood, and I will. But you can't stay here because they are sure to come right away here. —Don Braulio, of all men, with so many relatives!—Listen. You have to go and hide with the Indians and stay with them at their rancheria on the other side of the ridge until things blow over. You must go tonight, right away. This girl here will show you the trail." Here he turned to my mother: "You tell the old Lalihesi that I sent him." She said, *"Si señor,"* my mother did. She hated to go, but what else could she do but say yes? No one ever said no to Don Bartolomeo, especially not when he was angry and gave his orders. So my father threw his cigarette into the fire, said *"Bueno, pues"* with resignation, shrugged his shoulders, and smiled at his sister-in-law. And off they went into the night, he and my mother; and that is how I was born.

two

Don Leandro—that was my father's name—did not stay long at the rancheria, although everyone there liked him. (My mother said you couldn't help liking him.) He was forever running down to the ranch on the other side of the ridge. And finally he ran off with Doña Mercedes.

Don Bartolomeo must have expected it because the old Lalihesi—he was our chief and a paternal grand-uncle of my mother, and he was also a kind of foreman on the ranch—told me that he was with Don Bartolomeo when it happened. They had been running wild cattle for two days in the *ciénaga,* but the cattle were too wild and they had to let them go.

Don Bartolomeo had two boys, but they were too young to ride then, and none of the Indians except the old Lalihesi were good *vaqueros*—and as for the *vaqueros* from Monterey and Salinas, they are no good for this wild coast—too steep for them. They get dizzy and let the cattle go.

Don Bartolomeo and the old Lalihesi had been trying for two days to get those wild cattle in the *ciénaga*. They camped there two nights, but what can two men do alone with wild cattle? So on the morning of the third day, they ate their last *empanadas* and started for home. They came to Pino Bonito about noon.

From there, you know, you can see up and down the ridge and all around—and there at a bend of the trail, down below, those two—my father and Doña Mercedes—came into view, riding away. The old Lalihesi expected Don Bartolomeo to gallop along the ridge trail. He could have reached the Sur long before them. But no, he sat on his horse, straight up, and never said a word. He never spoke and never moved for a long time—just kept looking way down at the ocean. At last, he turned to the old Lalihesi, and he said to him, "You go back to the rancheria and send me a woman to take care of the boys."

three

So my mother went back to the ranch to take care of Don Bartolomeo and his two boys. But she didn't want to go alone; she was afraid of Don Bartolomeo because he was always so silent and sombre. So she took an old aunt along with her, an old woman called Hilahilukeni.

That old woman was a witch. She could change herself into a

bear and travel about at night. She knew all kinds of spirits. I have often seen her go into the chaparral and talk to them. And she could cure any kind of sickness if she wanted. She hated the Spaniards. She was one of the very few who ever came back from the mission at Carmel. She had learned to speak the other language there, the language of the Carmel Indians. But she never learned Spanish—only a few words.

I was born soon after my mother went back to Don Bartolomeo's house, and so I grew up with his sons and we all learned to be *vaqueros*. Don Bartolomeo and the old Lalihesi were our teachers, and hard teachers they were. If we got hungry, they only laughed and told us to eat brush like the deer.

"Look, boys," the old Lalihesi would say, "look, look at all this fine, juicy chaparral, all this *yerba del oso;* any of you hungry? Eat, eat plenty of it," and he would sing the old song:

Arriba, muchachos, arriba!
Arrimense las botas,
Porque vamos á Monterey
A comer puras bellotas.

Then he would give a yell and make his horse dance. Of course, we would laugh, but Don Bartolomeo would not even smile. He kept riding along the trail, always straight in the saddle, as if nothing existed but himself and his thoughts. But all the same it was always he who saw the cattle first. He would stop suddenly, looking steadily across the *cañada* when we boys could see nothing but monte and brush shining in the glare of noon and the blue jays chattering all around us.

But presently, the old Lalihesi would say, "Yes, I see him. That's the *aguililla* we lost last year. *Orejano,* too. *Por Dios,* what eyes you have, master! See, boys, the blue jays are making fun of you, *por malos vaqueros.* Shame on you, to let two old men beat you with their old eyes!"

He was always joking and playing, the old Lalihesi. He was the only man who ever joked in the presence of Don Bartolomeo, but he was not afraid of him. He liked him and obeyed him in everything that was not really Indian affairs, but he was not afraid of him. And my uncle would often ask his advice because the old chief was very wise and experienced in spite of his jokes. The Lalihesi gave me all my Indian education and told me about the animals who were people, and the spirits who live in certain trees and rocks.

Each little *cañada*, each little ravine, especially those where water runs, belongs to a spirit who lives there. You must speak to him when you go by, otherwise he will be angry. And if you remember his name, all the better. Then he is pleased, and he will give you good luck. The old Lalihesi taught me all these things when we rode alone, he and I, and we spoke in our own language.

And I learned some things, too, from that old Hilahilukeni woman at the ranch. She would tell me things sometimes if she was in good spirits, which was seldom. Most times she said she did not know and grumbled something about my being a Spaniard, and why should I want to know these things. She was a very bad-tempered old woman, and she didn't do any work. She was too old for that. She just sat in the sun in front of the house looking at the coast and over at the ocean and muttering, muttering all the time, in a language that nobody understood. Everyone was afraid of her except Don Bartolomeo. He never took any notice of her.

four

My uncle, Don Bartolomeo, was not of Monterey. He came from Mexico or Spain or some place far from here. I don't know why he settled here. I have often thought about that, but I never could account for it. He could have settled on those large flats at the mouth of the Sur, where Cooper settled later on and raised so many cattle and horses. And there were lots of other better places between here and the mission at Carmel.

Why should he have wanted to come so far, so far into this wild country where it is so steep everywhere? I don't know, I don't know. Maybe it was because he liked the beauty of it, maybe because he wanted to forget and get away as far as he could, and maybe he just made a mistake and would not admit it.

He was a proud man, silent and tall, and he never seemed to see anyone. In the long evenings of winter when it rained and rained outside, he walked up and down the room or he sat in front of the fire, but he never spoke.

That old woman Hilahilukeni, she crouched in her corner and mumbled and muttered to herself. The boys and I made *reatas, cuartas, riendas,* all sorts of braided leather work. I was best at it because I was more patient than my cousins. The old Lalihesi had taught me. My mother sat on the floor after she had cleared away the eating things and made baskets.

It was a lonely place, especially in winter when the fog came in from the sea and rushed through the big trees. Nobody ever rode this way, except once in a while a friend of Don Bartolomeo who came out to hunt bears.

His name was Don Faustino, and I think he and my uncle had come from the same place, for I used to hear them sometimes when they talked by the fire in the evening, and they said: *"En nuestra tierra . . ."* and they talked of people I have never heard anyone else mention. That was when the two of them were alone, but usually Don Faustino came to the ranch with several friends —sometimes four or five of them—all of them wild to hunt bears.

All of these people treated my uncle with great respect and deference, and he was always very courteous with them, but he never unbent from his dignity. Don Faustino was very wealthy, and so were all his friends, I think, because they dressed in fine style, with *botas vaqueras* of finest leather, beautiful shirts of soft linen, and sashes of beautiful colors of silk. And all of them had much silver on their saddles and riding outfits.

It looked strange to see them in that wild place of ours where everything—chairs, tables, walls—was rough and hewn with the axe and we ourselves half the time in rags patched up with rawhide or badly made buckskin with half the hair still sticking on. But on these occasions, Don Bartolomeo would get out his fine clothes, though he didn't dress like them at all. He was all in black, and he wore constantly a *capa* of broadcloth which he wrapped around him so well that it seemed to be alive and move of itself. And that way he looked very imposing. But he did not take any part in the hunt, although he was glad enough to see the bears done away with because they killed so many of his cattle every year.

Hunting did not interest him. So he stayed around the house and corrals and gave orders and saw that everything went well, because there were always a lot of people at the ranch on these occasions. Don Faustino and his friends brought along their servants and camping things and riders from their ranches, and some of them had Indians—those who owned ranches in the Carmel Valley. All of our Indians came, too, to help us, but it was really mostly for a chance to talk with those Carmel Indians and get news from their own people who had been taken away.

But the old Lalihesi always disappeared on those occasions. He went away somewhere, and did not come back until it was all over. Yet he was a good hunter and brave. Several bears he had killed himself alone, in his time, with his bow and arrow. But he said that you must not hunt bears in this way.

You must prepare yourself for it and do all the things a hunter should do and fast and clean yourself and keep away from all impure things for four days; then you must smoke to the masters of the hunt and tell them to give you luck; then smoke to the bear himself, and ask his permission and tell him not to be angry. "Then," he said, "you need not fear; luck will be on your side. But not this way, with all this noise and hubbub and everybody mixed up and women all around. That's a crazy way to do it—like a lot of children chasing a pig. They are liable to make a mistake and get after the wrong bear—some bear that *is* somebody—and then someone will be hurt. That's not the way to do it. It's not good, it's not good."

And sure enough, they did get hurt sometimes. The bear would often break the *reatas,* even after they had lassooed him—and then look out! Don Faustino almost got killed once that way. He was rather short, very quick and active, but a little fat and short of breath. And when they got the bear cornered he would get terribly excited and shout, lose his head entirely, and take great risks. He and Aurelio were always the most daring of all the hunters.

five

Aurelio was the younger of my two cousins, and full of life and fun. He could tame any horse and wasn't afraid of the wildest ones. Some young horses had been on the range five or six years. They were not even branded; we lived so far from anyone there was no need for it, and you know, horses do not stray like cattle. The *caballada* ran on the ridge, all the way from where it drops into the Sur, back to Aguas Calientes.

All of that ridge was covered by our horses running in the pines and *madroños*. There were several stallions. They fought and kept the *caballada* broken up into several bands. Sometimes we came across one of these bands in the springtime when the horses were getting fat and sleek, and there might be a proud colt running and stepping high.

Then this Aurelio, my cousin, would give a yell, "There goes my horse!" "If you catch him," the old Lalihesi would laugh. Aurelio then would get his *reata* ready and go ahead and wait until we drove the band along the ridge as fast as they would go. Then he would try to lasso his colt. He was not very good with the *reata,* but sometimes he did succeed. Then he would throw him down, and after we had helped him put on his saddle, he would ride the colt right on the open ridge with the ocean three thousand feet below.

There was no horse that could throw him. They might buck and whirl and go sideways all they pleased, they could not shake him off the saddle; and some of the young stallions were so wild they squalled; yes, they squalled with rage and struck out with their front feet and turned their heads around trying to bite him! But he would sit in the saddle and quirt them on the nose and laugh and laugh. He would rake them with the spurs from shoulder back to the tail, and you could see the long winter hair just fly on both sides like dandelion seeds.

The old Lalihesi would yell and almost roll off the saddle with laughter. Don Bartolomeo did not even smile. Sometimes he did not even look, but sat straight on his horse and gazed over the ocean. But Abelardo—that was my other cousin, the older one of the two brothers—he looked and looked, and his eyes burned with jealousy. He was not a good rider at all. He was one of the best men with a *reata* I ever saw, but he could not ride. When he rode a colt he got tense and stiff.

I don't think it was fear, but his temper was wrong. He did not want to fight. He hated to fight men, animals, or anything else. His temper was wrong. He was too proud. He was insanely proud. And he didn't want anything to beat him because he would die before he would quit. If he had to ride a bad horse, he would worry about it for days ahead and keep that horse in the corrals for days, and not ride him and not turn him loose, either. At last he would make up his mind and get us to saddle him, and it was a pity to see him, he was all white and sick.

And if the horse bucked hard he would grab the horn of the saddle or the saddle strings, anything he could, and he would hang on, hang on desperately, but he wouldn't quit and fall off.

When the horse quit bucking he would kick him to make him buck again and have to grab the horn once more. Sometimes he would ride a horse like that for a whole hour, fighting doggedly. I once saw him ride a big horse that bucked terribly hard—Abelardo was very tall and big and his horses had to be big and powerful, too—and that horse must have hit the ground as hard at every jump as a big bull. But Abelardo was hanging on. Pretty soon he started to bleed from the nose, and we shouted to him to quit—that it was enough. But, no, he kicked the horse every time he stopped bucking. That horse began to get tired.

He would stop in the middle of the corral with his head down, sullen. Then Abelardo would spur him and he would buck once more around the fence, and stop with his legs apart as if to brace himself. And Abelardo with blood all over his shirt would spur him again. It was awful. Well, at last, that horse lay down sideways, just gave up, couldn't fight any more. And Abelardo was leaning against the fence vomiting blood.

But it was foolish for Aurelio to ride an unbroken colt right out on the open ridge. Because, though most horses just bucked and fought, sometimes there would be one that hardly bucked at all but tried to run away. Now, when an unbroken colt wants to run and you have nothing but a jáquima around his nose, you cannot stop him; the best rider and the strongest man cannot stop him. You just have to take chances and stay on and hope he won't break his neck in a ditch. All that is bad enough around the corrals at home, but on the open ridge, right on top of everything, with the world going down both sides for thousands of feet, it was a foolish thing to do.

But Aurelio did not seem to know what danger was, or maybe he had too much spirit. Anyway, off they would go down the ridge, that boy and his horse, the colt half bucking, half running and Aurelio laughing, yelling, and waving his hat. And old Lalihesi would shout after him, "Look out, my boy, jump off in time if he makes for a *barranco*."

Old Lalihesi was very fond of Aurelio, but he scolded him

often. "You are no good; all you can do is ride wild horses. Why don't you take some interest in the ranch as your brother does. See how he works. He does all the work and you do all the whistling." And the funny part of it was that Aurelio never got angry with the old Lalihesi when he scolded him, while no one else could reprove him without his flying into a passion, except his father, of course. But then Don Bartolomeo never scolded, he never said anything, he only looked.

six

Abelardo was older than Aurelio and had a bigger frame; he was taller and had black eyes and black hair, while Aurelio was fair with blue eyes. Sometimes Abelardo would growl at Aurelio: "You never fed the horses last night; no one can trust you at all— you think about nothing but women and playing tricks. Why don't you take some interest in the ranch?" But Aurelio would flare up right away: "Go to hell with your ranch. I am tired of the ranch. I am going away. I am going away where there are people who speak. I am tired of grunting bears."

But Abelardo wouldn't dispute with him. He would only look sad and contemptuous, and this made Aurelio all the madder, and he would rail about the whole place—how wild and lonely it was, too steep, too much brush, too much mountain— everything wrong, a cursed place. And sometimes I came pretty near agreeing with him. There seemed to be a kind of curse about the country so that everything turned wild and wrong or disappeared or died like my people.

But one time, one of those crazy rides on the ridge almost ended badly. Aurelio had gone off yelling and playing on a runaway colt, and the old Lalihesi turned around and started to tease Abelardo: "Eh, it's not you who would do that!"

"No, I am not fool enough," growled Abelardo. "Some day he will break his neck."

"Break his neck! Break his neck! Not that boy; he is too quick—but," and he laughed maliciously, "that's just what you would like to see him do."

Don Bartolomeo here turned around in his saddle so suddenly that it startled us. His look was terrible. Lalihesi tried to laugh it off. "Nothing but a joke, master, nothing but a joke." The old man's face was pale, and his eyes were blazing. He looked very sharply at Abelardo, and Abelardo looked back at him without winking an eyelid. I felt very uncomfortable. I felt I didn't understand these people at all.

We started to go home, and after riding a little while, Don Bartolomeo asked Abelardo out of a clear sky: "Did you ever see your Uncle Leandro?"

"No; and I don't want ever to see him, either," was the reply. Don Bartolomeo did not say anything else, but he rode on, straight in the saddle as usual, looking incessantly all over the chaparral. The old Lalihesi lagged behind.

He was very much annoyed and put out, and he mumbled to me in our tongue, "Bad, bad, all this is bad. You never can joke with these people. They are mad; like all *mats-haiba*." (Sometimes he seemed to forget that my father, too, had been a *mats-haiba*, and sometimes I forgot it myself.) I tried to say something, but he was very surly and told me to shut up.

When we arrived at Pino Bonito, without saying a word the Lalihesi left us and turned down the trail that goes by the Aguaje de la Vírgen and crosses the arroyo further down. There was an Indian camping ground there at the crossing, and I think there were some of our people there at that time. He did not turn up at our ranch for nearly a week.

That evening, Aurelio had not come in at supper time, and we ate in silence. We were almost through when he arrived on foot and packing his saddle. His horse had jumped down a *barranco* and broken a leg. He himself had jumped off in time, but he had to kill the colt. And he fell to his food like a hungry wolf, laughing while he told us about the ride, with his mouth full and still cursing that colt. We were all very much relieved.

seven

One day, while plowing the lower field, Abelardo found one of those stone mortars that the Indians use for pounding acorns. Only this was a very large one. I think it was the largest one I have ever seen. It was about as high as the knee and very even and deep. It was made of a bluish sort of rock, well polished. He brought it home on the harrow when he was through harrowing and set it out on the open space in front of the stable, just on the edge of the cliff.

"There," he said, "that's the first stone of the great fence," and he laughed—a thing he seldom did—but that day he seemed to be in a good humor because he had finished the plowing and harrowing. Then he sat down on that mortar on the edge of the dizzy height and smoked a cigarette and looked at the ocean below him.

"We must make that fence, sooner or later, or some animal will fall over the cliff and get killed one of these days," and he laughed again. "How many times have we said that? Hundreds of times—either father, the old man, myself, or you. Why don't we make that fence? It would take only a couple of days to bring enough stones for a wall as high as a man's breast."

He looked down again. "It must be about a thousand feet high—perhaps even more. I wonder why father chose this site. Some day, I think the whole place, house, barn, and corrals, will fall into the sea; but no—it is all solid rock here. It will never slide."

Just then we heard the *vaquero's* yell above, and we turned and looked up, and there was Aurelio coming down the hill on his best horse and showing off. That was a fine horse, very well broken and sure-footed, and Aurelio was very proud of him. And there he was coming down as fast as he could, just for fun. It was very steep there just before reaching the flat where the house and corrals were built—one of those very steep places where a horse doesn't really gallop downhill, but bucks in big jumps. When he reached the flat, he barely pulled on the rein, and that horse sat down and slid for nearly twenty feet.

"Ha-ha! *Caballito de oro!*" He looked at us and laughed and gave another yell. He looked very beautiful sitting there on his excited horse—so easy, so proud. Then he got off and led his horse to the stable.

I turned back to Abelardo, and the look on his face gave me a shock. I have often thought about it, many and many a time. I have seen that face often at night, and I have tried to understand what it meant, but it has always puzzled me. It was set and hard and at the same time very soft as if he was going to cry. Then he shuddered, quick but all over, and moved off in the direction of the house.

Now the old Hilahilukeni woman had been sitting there all that time with her back to the barn. It was her favorite place in the afternoon, in the sun, to warm herself. That is where she sat always, growling and muttering in that language of the Carmel Indians. But this time she spoke in our own tongue. It startled me because she spoke so suddenly She was speaking to that big mortar that Abelardo had left on the ledge of the cliff.

"Do not be angry, stone. I have had nothing to do with it. None of the *effehi* has had any thought to disturb you. But you know who these *mats-haiba* are." She rolled a cigarette and she blew smoke toward the stone. Then she got up and went off into the chaparral, and I could hear her calling to her spirits. She had a thin, cracked voice, but she knew hundreds of songs. I did not know what to think of all that, but I did not like it much. Toward evening the old Lalihesi came back on his horse. He had been riding, looking after calves.

He saw me, and he asked, "How long has she been cackling there in the brush, the old hen, the old witch, the old she-bear? What is she up to again?" Then his eyes fell on the mortar, and he looked very much annoyed. He asked me, pointing to the stone mortar, "When did this fellow come here?" I told him that Abelardo had brought it on the harrow. He seemed a little relieved, but he still muttered.

"Those fool *mats-haiba* are always doing things like that. They don't know anything. That's bad; that's bad. It will bring bad luck to someone. That boy ought to know better. I have told him time and again to leave those things alone. You have to be a very strong doctor to deal with that kind of stone. See that old woman. Even she is afraid. But these fool *mats-haiba* don't know anything. Always nosing around carelessly, putting their heads into traps like a silly coyote. That's why we are all dying off. It's because of these *mats-haibas*. The spirits don't like them, and they leave our country. We have no protection. It's bad, it's bad. Have you any tobacco? Give me some." And he smoked to the stone for quite a while.

eight

At the end of the spring every year, when the grass was tall and full of seed, we gathered the fat cattle and drove them to Monterey. It was quite a difficult task because so many were wild. There were too few of us so some *vaqueros* always came from Monterey to help us. They were not much good on these steep hillsides. They made a lot of noise, but they really were dizzy half the time, and when the cattle started to run down toward a *cañada,* it was always one of us who had to jump and head them off. Aurelio was the quickest, but Abelardo was good, too.

Don Bartolomeo and the old Lalihesi were getting a little old and stiff for the saddle, but they knew just what the cattle thought all the time. They knew every place where the leaders and wild ones were likely to make a break, and they would warn us ahead.

Then when we crossed the Rio del Sur we were pretty safe. The cattle were in a new country. They did not know the cross trails and other places good for making a break and a run, and very soon they made a steady herd, going along easily if we did not drive them too fast.

It was slow going, though, and it took us three or four days to reach Monterey. Don Bartolomeo would always turn back at the crossing of the Sur. *"Bueno, muchachos, ya andais bien,"* and he went back to the ranch. Then the old Lalihesi became the captain of the *vaquerada*. Among the *vaqueros* there were a few half-breeds—Carmeleños—but they were more Spanish than Indian.

Now they became very brave, and if an old cow would make a break they would be off after her like arrows. And the boys and I could take it pretty easily. We had a lot of *empanadas* with us and some coffee tied in a blanket on the cantle of the saddle. At night we turned the cattle into some low place—some flat with a lot of grass. We always stopped a couple of hours before dark, that they might have time to fill themselves; and after that, being tired, they would lie down peacefully.

We made a fire and ate our *empanadas,* and soon everybody was asleep; but about the middle of the night it would get so cold and the ground was so hard that one by one everybody got up and came closer to the fire. We drank more coffee and talked and dozed. The *vaqueros* from the outside seemed to be a little afraid of us, especially of Abelardo—probably because he was so silent and so big. They were more chummy with Aurelio. He joked and teased them and would ask about San José and Salinas and other places far away.

The old Lalihesi was the only one who never woke up. He never carried any blanket, but lay down on the ground, stiff as a board, and snored all night; in the morning I had to shake him and shake him to wake him up. At the first streak of dawn we were always on the way.

By the time we got to Monterey, we all looked like a pack of wild coyotes—with red eyes, dirty faces, our clothes full of dust and cockleburs. "There come the wild ones from the south coast," people would say, and tease. "Catch them, hog-tie them before they escape. . . . Well, boys, is it true, what they say, that the coast fell into the ocean last winter?" And the hired *vaqueros* looked very proud and spurred their horses and held them in check at the same time, but we just grinned. It made me dizzy to see so many people, and I was timid.

Abelardo grumbled and looked angry. He thought they were making fun of us. But Aurelio seemed to know everyone. He greeted all sorts of people and laughed and gave his yell, and people came out of the houses, women and children, and waved to us. Aurelio would sometimes take a boy and lift him to his saddle. "I'll teach you to ride after the wild ones." And that boy would swell with pride.

We always had a welcome at the house of Don Faustino. "Here you are in your own house, *muchachos,* plenty of beds. Have a good time, do what you please." Aurelio was his favorite. Don Faustino was a rich man. He had a wife and many servants, but he had no children. But the old Lalihesi seldom stopped there. He preferred to ride back to the Carmel mission where there were many Indians—Gabrieleños, Carmeleños, Sureños—all mixed. Some of them were of our own people. He talked with them and exchanged news.

He often tried to persuade our people to come back to the coast, but they said the priests would catch them and punish them. They said they did not like it there because the priests made them work so hard, but they were afraid to disobey because the priests knew much magic medicine and would poison them if they tried to escape. But I myself think that they rather liked it there because they had plenty of food, regularly, and there were so many Indians all together.

Sometimes, I stopped at the house of Don Faustino, but I also liked to go with the old Lalihesi and talk with our people. I never felt comfortable at Don Faustino's house. There were too many people, and they kept going through the house, up and down the stairs, and always talking so fast that it made me dizzy.

Abelardo never stopped at Don Faustino's. He went there, paid his respects and excused himself in his grave manner.

"But, *que diantre!*" shouted the old man. "Can't you stop one night anyway?" "No, I am sorry, but I must go back. The old gentleman is all alone down there"; and he would ride back, still dusty and unwashed, through the streets, looking neither right nor left, and stop at the mission for the night.

There we both ate with the priests, although I would rather they had left me with the Indians, but they said my father was a nobleman and I must accept their hospitality. It was miserable enough because I was always afraid to speak in the presence of Abelardo, and Abelardo himself never said a word. The next morning, all three of us would start early for the coast, and a couple of weeks later Aurelio would come in.

He must have had a good time in Monterey because everybody was fond of him—he was so gay and reckless and good looking. They say the women were mad about him and that when he left the pueblo to come back to the ranch, it was always because he had to. But he never spoke of these things to us. Only once, when I asked him if it were true that he was in love with a certain girl. We were sitting on a rock, on top of the ridge, resting and giving our horses a chance to blow. He made me repeat my question, and then he laughed. "Listen, little brother," he said. "Never set your heart on a horse. You remember that pinto stallion I broke, and how carefully I broke him? I had him in a jáquima alone for nine months, and then with double reins for another nine months, eh, a year and a half before I put a bit in his mouth, and then he didn't need a bit; he knew how to stop and when to turn. Didn't I lose my heart to him, eh? Well, and the next spring he turned his hoof and he has been lame ever since. That's one. And that black mare with the white feet—you remember her—how pretty she was, so proud and so easy, well, you know where her bones are, in that gully. That's another. And the big gray that Abelardo wanted too much, and he killed himself, too.

"So now, I never fall in love with any horse anymore. When I lose one, I go up to the ridge and I look over the *caballada* and pretty soon I find one to my taste. Little brother, there are many horses yet on the mountain, *muchos caballos en la sierra, y muchas mujeres en las casas de Monterey, y todas son putas.*" I protested, "There are surely some good ones." But he sneered in an ugly way (the only time I ever saw him do that, not even when he was quarreling with Abelardo), and he added shortly, *"Ni la que me parió!"* And then he was silent.

It was getting late; the sun was almost in the water, and the deer were coming out of the woods in little bands to eat weeds in the open. Aurelio was looking at them, but I don't think he saw them because he was smiling in a kind of ugly grin. Presently he got up and said, "Let's go, it's getting late." But I had noticed smoke down in the arroyo, so I told him some of my people must be camping there and I thought I would go and see them. He said, *"Bueno, adiós,"* and started down the ridge, while I took the trail of the Aguaje de la Virgen.

The next year when we took the cattle to Monterey, he stayed in town a long time. We had been back at the ranch two weeks, and he had not come in yet. Three weeks—and he hadn't come back. He never came back for several years.

nine

One winter my mother died. She had been sick only a few days, and she died. The old woman, Hilahilukeni, tried to cure her. She was a good doctor, but she could not do anything. She said the spirits wouldn't help her. She sang and called to the spirits for three nights, but they didn't answer her.

She said there were not enough of us singing, and the spirits had retired to the tops of the mountains and could not hear us. Of course, there were only two of us helping her—the old Lalihesi and myself—and I knew only a few of the songs. The woman said the spirits were afraid of the Spaniards and had retired to the mountain tops, so she gave it up, and my mother died. It was at the close of the winter. I felt very bad after that; and I was lonely. Aurelio was gone, and the old Lalihesi often went and stayed for days and days at some Indian camp with the few Indians that were left. And at the ranch those two men hardly ever spoke.

I was a man now—just a grown man—and I began to feel queer and strange and lonely as if I was expecting something to happen. I often went out alone and traveled around. The whole place seemed lonely and full of things. I went into the deep ravines and smoked to the spirits and called to them. Sometimes, I stopped in open places and looked at the ocean until I grew dizzy and felt queer and sad. I often went and stayed at the Indian camp. There were only a few of my people left at that time, mostly old people. I don't know why all the Indians died so fast when the *mats-haiba* came.

There was a very old man. The old Lalihesi called him *metg*—grandfather. He must have been a relation of his, but I don't know just what relation. He was very old, and they said he was a powerful doctor, but he kept very much to himself and talked very little. One day he said to me, "You are a man now, but you have no name. Have you had a dream?" I told him I had not had the right dream yet, although I had often called to the spirits. "That's because you don't know, but I will tell you. In the fall of the year, when the turpentine weed is blooming and smelling strong on the hillsides, that's the time. Then you go to the Ventana ridge where there are fir trees growing near the top of the mountain. You must fast four days before you go, eat nothing between sunrise and sunset, and then only a handful of corn mush. Eat no meat, eat no abalones.

"Then, when you get there, wait until the sun is ready to drop into the water. Then you climb one of those trees. Climb to the very top where the cones are and take one. Now if it breaks in your hand—that means that the spirits have no use for you. But if the spirits like you, then it will hold firm in your hand. You hold it out to the north and to the south, to the east and to the west, and a spirit will come and take it from your hand. Then you will lose your mind, and you will fall, but the spirit that protects you will take hold of you and put you down on the ground. That spirit will give you back a new life, and he will protect you. You will live a long time. Now you try it this fall. Maybe you will be lucky, and the spirits will come to you. Maybe the spirits have no use for you."

I thought a great deal about it all summer. I wondered if the spirits would come to me. During the fall, when the turpentine weed smelled strongly on the hillsides, I did as he told me. I fasted for four days, and the fourth morning I started for the Ventana ridge. I traveled all day through the *cañadas* and the woods. I was all alone. I never liked to be alone in those places back from the ocean. I was weak from fasting. In the evening I got close to the top of the mountain.

There were many firs there. I tried to pick out a small tree, but only the tall trees bear cones, and the cones are very near the top. The tops of these trees are extremely slender. For the last thirty feet or so the trunk is just a flexible pole not much thicker than a man's arm. As I looked at them from down below I felt very doubtful. I thought it must surely break under my weight. But finally I saw a tree with several cones quite low. The sun was sinking in the sky so I made up my mind, and I started to climb that tree. I climbed fast at first, but when I got near the middle of the tree I began to grow tired. My hands were tired because I grew dizzy with the height, and I grasped the branches with too much force. I could feel my heart beating, beating, and a great feeling of fear came over me. But I wanted to be blessed by the spirits, and I kept on climbing, climbing, until I was within reach of the cones.

There were three of them, but each one, as soon as I grabbed it, broke in my hand. Oh! I felt very badly, then, for I thought the spirits had no use for me. Just then I saw one more cone, but this one was at the very top of the tree. I didn't have enough courage to climb after it. I knew for sure the top of the tree would break under my weight. But I was desperate, too. I wanted to be blessed by the spirits, and I thought if the spirits wanted me to get that cone they would hold me up, and if they did not I might as well be killed right there and then. So I kept on climbing, and the tree swayed with me. At last I got to the top, and I grabbed that cone in my hand. It was very prickly, but I didn't care. It did not break in my hand. The spirits were protecting me, and I was happy. I have never been so happy in my life. I wasn't dizzy any more. The sun was just touching the water, and all the world seemed to be burning. I could see everywhere around. There were cañons and woods and mountains all around. I was on top of the world. Oh! I felt happy.

Then I held the cone toward the sun, and then a great bird came—a great eagle—and I knew right away he was my spirit protector. He circled four times around the top of the tree, and the fourth time he flew close by and took the cone. Then I lost my mind, and everything grew dark; but that eagle took me and put me down on the ground, and there I lay for a long time. I don't know how long, but when my mind came back it was night, and I could see the stars sparkling through the trees. I felt very happy there, and I did not want to move. I couldn't think just who I was, but I felt happy.

Very soon, I thought I heard singing, and then I saw a lot of Indians come by. They passed very close to me, but they did not seem to see me. They kept coming, more and more of them, and passing on. There were some I recognized—Indians I had known and who had died. I called to them, but they did not hear me. They kept on passing, passing, until at last I grew tired. There were many, many of them. It made me dizzy to see them passing by. I closed my eyes then, and I fell asleep.

I don't know how long I slept. It must have been a long time.

When I woke the sun was high in the sky, and it was hot. I felt terribly sore in my limbs and all over my body—as if someone had beaten me with a stick—but I felt very happy just the same because I knew that the spirits liked me. So I got up and did as the old man had told me to do. I went straight down the mountain without ever looking back, and I stopped four times, and each time I took tobacco and smoked to the spirits.

It was almost dark when I reached the Indian camp. The old man was sitting a little way off. He saw me coming, but he never called me and never said anything. There was an old woman sick in the camp, and he was going to sing for her that night. He sang all that night and doctored her. He sang many songs. He sang the song of the bear and the quail song and the manzanita song and the redwood tree song—all the songs. But when he sang the eagle song I felt a great feeling come all over me like a cloud; a great happiness just like that moment at the top of the tree, and I lost my mind again. I do not know how long it was, but I do not think it was long because when I came to my senses they were still singing.

The next morning that old doctor called me aside, and he called me by my new name. And he told the old Lalihesi about it. I also told it to another man, a brother of my mother who was living then in the Carmel mission. But I never told anyone else what my Indian name was. However, that old woman at the ranch, that old witch Hilahilukeni, she found it out, somehow. At least, I think she did, because I heard her several times grumble something that was pretty close to it in meaning. I did not like it at all, but she never did me any harm. I do not know how she could have learned it, except that she was always talking with the spirits.

ten

One day Don Faustino arrived at the ranch. It was in the evening. He had ridden all day from town, and he was all alone. He seemed much worried and hardly spoke during supper. Then he had a long talk with my uncle. It seemed that Doña Mercedes, Don Bartolomeo's wife who had run away with my father, you know, had come back, very poor and very sick, and with her a grown daughter. She was broken down and very repentant, and she wanted Don Bartolomeo to forgive her.

Abelardo and I were sitting on the porch smoking, and we could hear them talking inside, or rather, we could hear Don Faustino, because Don Bartolomeo was not saying a word. He pleaded and pleaded with him for a long time: "She is dying, I tell you. You must go and forgive her." But my uncle only said, "No." And again, "No!" Then Don Faustino got very angry and reproached him very hard. I had not imagined that anyone would ever dare to speak to Don Bartolomeo in that way.

"You have no heart. You are not a Christian. It is your damnable pride. But you are becoming an old man. Look out. It is dangerous not to forgive. It was your fault, yes, your fault, your own fault. You were mad enough to bury a young woman in this desert, but you are mad, you are mad. Mad like your own uncle. Your insane pride has ruined your life, and you, in turn, have ruined all the lives around you. In the name of God, listen to me who have been your friend since we were little boys, and my father was your father's friend.

"Listen to me; in the name of God, be human. That poor woman has suffered, and she is dying. Go to her and forgive her." His voice had risen higher and higher. And then my uncle spoke, very slowly, almost in low tones, as if tired and weary. "You don't understand, Faustino, you don't understand. It is not her. Her I have forgiven long ago and forgotten. Tell her to die in peace—

that I have forgiven her. I have forgiven her long ago. She has ceased to exist for me—don't bother me with her; I don't care about her. It is the other one that I won't forgive." There was a pause, and then Don Faustino said in a puzzled voice, "But he is dead."

"Yes, but I have not forgiven him, and I don't forgive him, and I will not forgive him even on the day of the Last Judgment!" My uncle thundered those last words, and after that there was an unbroken silence.

After a while Don Faustino came slowly out on the porch. His face was puzzled and full of pain. He looked all around in a bewildered way and then noticed us. "Boys, it is terrible. That man is mad. I have known him all my life, but I don't understand. Yes, it is the curse coming back again. Abelardo, Abelardo, my son, I am your godfather. I held you at the baptismal font. You will come and hold your mother in your arms before she dies." But Abelardo turned his face away. "The only mother I remember was an Indian woman who raised me, and she died last year."

Don Faustino left the ranch early the next morning. He woke me at dawn and asked me to saddle him a fresh horse. He embraced me before he mounted. "You come and see me whenever you ride to town, my boy. You be sure to come and tell me how things are drifting here."

"But, Don Faustino, aren't you coming to hunt bears?"

"No, no, I am never coming back. I don't want to see this country again. I am afraid of it. There must be a curse here. Forgive me for saying that, my boy, but it is not the same for you. Your mother's blood will save you."

"Yes, yes, I know, Don Faustino, I know there is a curse here. We all know there is a curse."

"Ah, you also know it." He shook his head very sadly, embraced me again, and rode off.

eleven

I saw Don Faustino again the following summer when we drove the cattle to Monterey. He sent for me as soon as he heard I was in town. "Listen, boy," he said, after embracing me warmly. "You must tell your uncle to take that girl. I can't hold her. My wife can't hold her. Nobody can hold her. She drives us crazy. You have never seen her, have you? Well, she is Aurelio, and she is your father, all over again. She has all the young men of the town running after her—nothing but dances and *fiestas* and parties in the country—and then they come and serenade at night under her windows, and my poor wife and myself—we can't sleep. I can't stand it any longer—I can't, I can't. That girl is too much for me.

"Then she goes to my ranch and turns everything topsy-turvy. You ought to see her ride. Why, she rides better than a man—but she has no sense. She rides my best horses to death. She has all the *vaqueros* mad, all in love with her, just like the señores in town.

"And even old Cipriano, my foreman; she has him wound around her little finger. He begs me not to let her come there. 'We cannot do anything there, Don Faustino, when that girl comes,' he says, 'She takes all the *vaqueros* hunting with her, and then they quarrel and fight among themselves. She got them to teach her to lasso, and she has already broken a cow's leg, and she nearly cut off her own thumb with the *reata*. She will kill herself some day. And she rides the best horses at a gallop all day. She herself never gets tired, no; but the horses have to be rested for a week after.'

"That's what Cipriano says to me. And then, the next time she goes there, she turns her eyeballs up at him, and she is pretty, you know—she is damn pretty. 'Uncle Cipriano, little grand-father, may I have a horse today? Just a good old plug will do for me.' And Cipriano goes right over to the corral and picks her out the most lively one with thin legs and little feet.

"And she does me and my wife just the way she does old Cipriano. That girl will get into trouble. She is brave and fearless, and she orders her gallants around like slaves. But she does not know what she wants. But I know. I know, and I don't want to be responsible. I promised Mercedes (may God rest her soul). Well, she is your sister, my boy—only you haven't any of that in you, God bless you. You are all your mother." And he embraced me again, warmly.

"Well, you must tell your uncle to take her—it's the only way. I can't hold her, my wife can't; but maybe the life there will. My God! It's awful to send that girl there—it's not the place for her—but where else? And I know she can't turn your uncle around her little finger. It's going to be hard for him, but, by God, he deserves it; he deserves it.

"And Abelardo is her brother, too—only I don't understand that boy—where is he, by the way? Stayed at the mission last night, eh? As usual, the bear! But you will be kind to her, I know. You are the only sane one in that bunch. Well, well, I am sorry, but it must be done. You be sure to tell your uncle when you go back."

So I told Don Bartolomeo when we got back to the ranch. He listened in silence. He was looking away at the ocean. I thought he had not listened to me at all. But he said, "Get several pack horses. No doubt she has many things with her."

twelve

Well, she was an extraordinary woman, that girl who was a daughter of my father. When I arrived in Monterey, in the courtyard of Don Faustino's house, I was very dusty and tired. I had made the trip in one day, and I had brought her a good horse, too.

I had begun to take off the saddles, and there she was right in the midst of the horses with all her flounces and red lips and her eyes. She called me "elder brother" in our own Indian tongue. This is the only word she knew, I think, and she must have learned it just to please me. And she kissed me very softly. Now that part of it was not at all Indian. Besides, no woman had ever kissed me. Besides, she was my own blood. I lost control right there and then, and she always ruled me after that.

But that is not the way she met Abelardo. It was on Pino Bonito we met him. He knew we were coming, and he was waiting for us. That is, he knew we would get there just about that time—about an hour before sundown. Maybe he had come two or three days in succession. It was so lonely at the ranch. Concha had been very much excited ever since we reached the real coast, our coast. She said she had never seen such a beautiful place—not anywhere—although she had traveled a great deal with her mother. We had been two days on the road on account of pack horses, but she did not seem tired at all.

And then we saw him, or rather we saw first his big black horse tied to a tree, and the horse whinnied to our animals. Abelardo had been lying down on the pine needles under the Pino Bonito, I suppose, and he shambled forward toward us just like a big bear coming out of the brush. He was a very big man, you know. If it had been Aurelio, now, he would have jumped on his horse with a whoop and a yell and made him buck or some crazy trick like that, but Abelardo just came forward and stood in front of Concha and removed his hat.

"*Sea Vd. la bienvenida,*" he said. He said it very gravely. And she sat there on her horse like a fool—not answering him at all, and very pale. I think he gave her a fright coming out of the shade that way so silently. So he turned to me and asked me if we had a good trip, but I was so surprised at his speaking to her with "*Vd.*" instead of "*tú*" that I didn't have wit enough to answer him.

He must have thought somebody had turned us dumb on the trip. "Well, it is getting late. Let's start down," he said, as gravely as ever. All the way down the ridge I kept thinking about his calling her *"Vd."* instead of *"tú."* Because, you see, he was only her half brother just like me, but on the other side, and I had called her *"tú"* right from the start.

And I worried about other things, too. Things behind that, and that was the first time of my life when I felt wrong because I was a half-breed and not one full thing or the other. As for Concha, she had gotten over her fright, if fright it was, and now she was red and white in turns and in a vexed mood.

Once her horse hesitated at a rock, and she gave him such a cut with the whip that he leaped right over it. It was a bad place in the trail but she was light and her horse was a good one. But Abelardo gave a low whistle and shook his head.

That put her in the van, and it was she who led us into the ranch. Don Bartolomeo was sitting on a bench at the back of the house. He never made a move when he saw us, but she jumped off her horse and walked straight to him and knelt in front of him. I was so interested in watching them that I let the pack horses get into a tangle in front of the corral gates. I wanted to see what he would do and say. But he did not say anything.

Only after quite a while he raised his hand, and with his thumb he made the sign of the cross on her forehead, and I saw his lips move. I guess he was blessing her. I could see only her back, of course, and it was shaking, and I knew she was crying and sobbing with her face buried in her hands.

But he never moved and never said a word. Then Abelardo called to me from the corral to help him unpack. It was almost night now. I could hardly see the ropes and got all tangled up and mad. And I could hear the old Hilahilukeni woman out in the chaparral calling to her spirits, and I was so angry that if I had not been so afraid of her I would have cursed her.

I was glad to have a woman around the ranch again. I was tired of cooking, and the house had become very dirty and messy. But Concha was not a house woman at all. She was out on her horse all the time, and I had to do the cooking just as before.

Then, too, I had expected that it would not be so lonely and gloomy as before. But it was worse, if anything, because now Abelardo seemed all queer. He changed his mind all the time.

He started to go out riding, and before an hour he was back. Then he'd commence to fix a fence or something near the house, and then he'd start something else. And Concha, she was worse. Sometimes she sat on the porch, all dressed up and perfumed. I had to make two more trips to town to bring all her things and dresses—boxes and boxes. Then she would jump up and run into her room and put on man's clothes, and look more like a woman than ever.

"Abelardo, oh, Abelardo!" she would call. "May I have a horse?" And Abelardo would saddle her a horse without saying a word; and off she would go, he looking after her; then he would sit on that big mortar and look over the ocean and do nothing for hours, and that was not at all natural for him.

He seemed to be afraid of her, and she of him—because she joked and played with me freely enough, but she hardly ever spoke to him or even looked at him. But he looked at her all the time with that strange hard stare of his—half hatred, half scorn—yet never surely either the one or the other. As for Don Bartolomeo, he seemed to have retired entirely into his thoughts and hardly ever spoke to any of us.

Concha had brought a new guitar, and she used to sing in the evenings; queer songs she sang—half sad, half angry—that made you feel almost mad. At least, this is the way I felt, and it must have been the same with Abelardo because he began to sleep badly, turning over and over so much that he disturbed me; and I made him move his bed to the other end of the room—the two boys and I always slept upstairs in a large room, a sort of attic— and he blamed it on the songs. He said he could hear them in his sleep.

thirteen

The winter came. It was a long winter with much rain and fog. The old Lalihesi stayed with us for a little while. He and Concha made friends right away. She was more natural with him than with anyone else. I wish he had remained with us, but finally he said that he had come to say good-by.

"There are too few of us left and only very old ones," he told me, "so we have decided to go over to Jolon and stay with the Indians there. Some of us have got relations among them, and they have a good rancheria. I know a little of their language."

I wanted to go with him. I told him I didn't like to stay here, but he wouldn't let me. "You belong here. You belong with your uncle. It would not be right for you to leave them. I know, I know what you mean and what is in your head. You had better not speak about it. I don't like it, either. But you know he is your elder brother, in our way of speaking, and so it's not for you to say anything. After all, they are Spanish, and it's their own way."

Don Bartolomeo talked a good deal with the Lalihesi; they talked about old things, and at the last he embraced him very tightly. But after he went Don Bartolomeo fell back into his mood.

The winter passed, and when the spring came that girl got more restless than ever; and to escape it I used to go out a great deal and look after the cattle. They needed it, too. They were getting very wild and half of them were *orejanos* calves. You see, all that winter Abelardo had done nothing but go around looking for something else, and the old man hardly ever got on a horse now, so I thought to myself:

"Well, if you won't do the *vaquero* work, you'll have to cook and look after the house. Because that girl is absolutely useless." Sometimes she came riding with me, especially at first, but she did not know a thing about the minds of cattle, and nearly every time she scared them into a wild run.

She enjoyed it. She was a marvelous rider and fearless—perhaps one of the best I have ever seen after Aurelio. And she would tear after them, yelling. Very soon our cattle got so wild you could not come in sight of them without their making for the woods. After that I went alone. I used to tie my horse in a clump of trees a little way from the house, and after breakfast I would watch for my chance and slip out. Then I would be obliged to laugh to myself all during the day, thinking of the picture: Abelardo—as big as a bear—in the kitchen and Concha, all painted up and perfumed with her ruffles and her pretty legs, sitting on the porch fanning herself. It was a hot summer that year, hot and still.

One evening we were still eating supper when the dogs barked, there was a yell and a whoop, a horse slid and stopped right in front of us in a cloud of dust, and out of it all jumped Aurelio, laughing and yelling. Even Don Bartolomeo smiled and gave him the blessing. Then Aurelio came and embraced me first and Abelardo who stood behind me, and then he kissed Concha just the same way. Then he held her off at arm's length.

"God be praised, but how handsome you are. They told me you were, but I didn't imagine it, little sister. You smell like a real woman." She blushed, of course. Then he gave her another kiss, and paying no more attention to her he went to the old Hilahilukeni where she sat all huddled against the wall like a heap of rags. And he took her and raised her and shook her and embraced her and called her an old witch, and she giggled in her high, thin, cracked voice.

We sat up till the middle of the night listening to his stories. He had been all over the world from San José down to San Diego, and he told us how they did things on all the big ranches. It was very interesting. Even after we went to bed I could not sleep thinking of it all, but Aurelio snored like a wild horse.

As soon as Aurelio came back everything changed. The very first time that he went riding with me, and she came along, too, things changed. She scattered the cattle, as usual, and Aurelio

swore a whole string of blasphemies. And he told her to go back
to the ranch. He swore at her, too, up and down.

She got mad and struck him in the face with her whip. It was
a pretty hard blow and left a red line that began to swell. She
looked at him without saying anything for a while—then she
burst into tears and galloped away on her horse. But what surprised me most was that he was not angry at all. He looked after
her as if he admired her. He only said, "She rides very well, but
she is a woman just the same, and the more she puts on men's
clothes the more she is a woman. I never saw one like her."

But after that she never came riding with us any more. She
was angry with him and would not speak to him for several days.
But he teased her out of it. Nobody could resist him—he was so

gay and handsome. And he even made her cook so Abelardo
could come riding with us. Only Abelardo was not changed. Aurelio asked me about it. "What is the matter with him? What is he
mad about? He looks as if something were eating him inside."

"I don't know," I said. "That's the way he has been all
winter."

Concha, now full of gayety, seemed to have forgiven Aurelio
entirely and to admire him very much. Both of them played a
good deal around the place and teased each other and laughed and
joked.

fourteen

It was a very hot summer with sultry nights. One night I woke up
with a bad feeling. I think I had too many blankets on me. I tried
to fix my bed again, and I had to light the lamp. I noticed that the
beds of the boys were empty, but I thought they must have gone
to sleep outside because it was so hot, and I paid no attention to
it. I was soon asleep again. When I woke up it was full daylight,
and I hurried into my clothes because that day we were to bring
some cattle down from the ridge, and we should have started just
at dawn.

So I was not surprised to see Abelardo standing in front of
the barn. Only when I came near, his face gave me a shock: it was
all set in a kind of grimace, and his eyes were red as if he had not
slept at all. "What's the matter with you?" I asked. But he only
grumbled, "Nothing—go in and feed the horses." Just then I saw
Aurelio coming out of the house. We both looked at him. He
walked in a queer, uncertain way, with his head hanging down,
like someone in deep thought. When he came nearer, I could see
that he, too, had not slept. Abelardo pushed me into the stable

then. "Go on, I tell you, and feed the horses."

But I had hardly taken hold of the fork when I heard Abelardo's voice say distinctly, "You are going to die." He said that very slowly, but his voice trembled. Then Aurelio's voice, "And why?"

"Because of what you did last night."

And then almost immediately I heard a shot. I rushed to the door, and I saw Abelardo with a smoking pistol in his hand. He was looking at something over the edge of the cliff. His face was full of horror and of pain. I saw Don Bartolomeo come running out of the house. And soon after Concha came, too, in her night-gown. Abelardo turned with the pistol in his hand and for a moment seemed bewildered; and I thought he was going to run.

But he saw his father and stopped dead. Don Bartolomeo came toward him. "Where is Aurelio, where is your brother?" Abelardo did not answer, but looked straight at his father. Then the old man took a step forward and roared again, "Where is your brother?"

When Don Bartolomeo took that step forward, Abelardo stepped back, still looking steadily at his father. Don Bartolomeo took another step forward, and Abelardo retreated again, but this time he stumbled against the big stone mortar. He lost his balance and fell over backward with just one sigh.

When he was just going to stumble against the mortar, I saw Concha raise her hands and clutch her throat and shake her head violently. No one moved for a while, then Don Bartolomeo raised his hands to the sky and in a terrible voice he cried, *"Ay! mis hijos, mis hijos!"* Then he seemed to notice the presence of the girl.

She was still clutching her throat and shaking her head. He seemed bewildered at her presence there in her nightgown. Then he covered his face with his hands and mumbled, *"Que horror, que horror!"* again and again, *"Que horror!"* and he stumbled away toward the house, moving his hands from him as if trying to push some vision away.

Then I ran. I broke and ran. I don't know where I went. I just

ran and ran, uphill and downhill, in and out of the cañons. I called
to all the spirits I knew to keep me from understanding, and I
waited for the night to cover it all up.

I sang all night to the spirits. I was very much afraid. In the
morning I came back to the ranch. I don't know why I came back.
I did not want to, but I thought of the horses tied in the stable and
nobody to feed them or water them. Besides I was hungry.

fifteen

When I went into the house I saw Don Bartolomeo sitting on a
chair. He did not speak or move when I came in. Later, Concha
came in, and he did not move or speak. He stayed that way all day.
After a while I realized that Concha had become dumb. There was
something very wild on her face, especially when she looked at
Don Bartolomeo. Sometimes she stood looking straight at him
with such hatred in her look that I thought surely he must feel it
and look up. But he never seemed to notice her or me.

After that I stayed as little as possible in the house. I was
afraid of them. I went out riding and stayed out all day long. I had
caught a colt and commenced to break him, just to do something.

One night I woke up in a fright. Don Bartolomeo was
standing over me with a lamp in his hand. "Where are the boys?"
he asked. "Where are my sons?" I thought he was crazy, and I did
not answer. Then he went with his lamp to their beds and came
back to me—"I cannot find them," he mumbled. "They are not in
their beds." Then he mumbled something else and went out.

He came back again night after night. He never spoke to me
during the day, but at night he would creep upstairs with his lamp
and wake me up and ask me absurd questions. "It was not I, was
it?" he would say, "Why did he do it?" "Do what?" I asked. But he

merely said, "Ah," and went out on tiptoe.

Almost every night he came now. "What do they do among your people when a thing like that happens? What is your law?"

"We have no law," I answered. "We don't do that." And again he said, "Ah," and went out.

But he would come back and bother me again until I lost all respect for him. "I didn't do it, did I?" He seemed to beg me to say that he had not, but I would not answer and turned my face to the wall. I just dreaded to hear his steps coming up at night—and his questions.

Then one day he told me to saddle him his horse. "I heard the boys driving cattle up there on the ridge. They must need help." I told him I had turned his horse loose and it would take me a long time to bring in the *caballada*.

"I will ride your horse then."

"But he is not broken yet. I have only had him in the jáquima."

"And do you think I am too old to turn a colt's head?" he blazed. "I'll bend his neck if it is made of iron. Bring him!" he roared.

So what could I do but obey him? I warned him that the colt had tried to run away with me several times, but he flared up at me, "Shut up, you little fool. I broke horses before your mother conceived you." And off he went. He stayed out several hours and came back finally looking very sad and old. And while I was un-saddling the horse, he sat on the stone mortar, and he began to cry silently. Once I thought I heard him say, "Abelardo, *mi hijo,* Abelardo."

He did not go out that way again for quite a while. But the same idea came back into his head that he had heard his sons driving cattle on the ridge, and he was bound that he would go. After that it became a daily matter. It worried me to see him get on that colt. Not that I thought he would spoil the horse—he knew more about it than I did—but after all, he was an old man, and if a colt runs, no one, however strong, can turn its head with a jáquima, and an old man is too stiff to jump. Well, that is just what happened.

I was standing in front of the barn plaiting a *reata* one day, when I saw them coming down that steep place behind the barn, the colt running away. I jumped and yelled and threw out my arms. The colt stopped in jerks and stood shaking, trembling, and snorting, and Don Bartolomeo cursing him for a stubborn fool. "Something scared him," he said to me. "Something in the bushes, out there. Some beast, I think—a bear, maybe."

The next day I went and rounded up the *caballada* and got him his horse, the one he used to ride before. But would not ride him now. "I like that colt of yours," he said. "He will make a good horse. He is a little headstrong, and that's just why I don't want you to ride him. You don't know. It takes the old one like me to soften their necks."

But he ran away again, just the same way—only this time I

wasn't at the corral. I was in front of the house when I saw them tearing down the steep place. I knew right away it was for the last time, but still I ran as fast as I could toward the stable to jump in front of the colt and stop him. But Don Bartolomeo seemed to have lost his head and gone mad because he was spurring the colt and beating him with his hat and yelling like a madman.

When the colt got to the edge of the cliff, he tried to stop himself, but he made just one jerk and went right over. That jerk shot Don Bartolomeo out of the saddle. I saw him for just an instant against the sky; his arms and legs spread out and his white hair flying. That's all I saw because I heard a scream behind—a horrible scream and a peal of laughter, a woman's laughter, and I ran and ran as I did that other time. I ran through the woods and cañons. I ran all day.

sixteen

Two days and two nights I stayed out. I was not far from the ranch, but I was afraid to come near. But I got very hungry, and the third morning I crept into the house. There was nobody in, and I started to eat. Then I heard a baby's crying. That scared me, and I ran out of the house. Then I thought I must have imagined it, and I went back. And again I thought I heard that baby. Then I listened, and this time I heard Concha calling me from her room in a very feeble voice.

She was not dumb anymore—only she was not much more than a ghost. She said things, but there was no meaning to them. I knew she was going to die, and I hoped so because nobody wants to live with a ghost, only I hoped, also, she would live long enough—at least until that baby learned to eat—because I didn't want him to die. One day she disappeared, and I never saw her

again. I knew well enough where she was, but I was always afraid
to look down.

I did not know it was so much pleasure to raise a child—
trouble, too, but more joy than trouble. He is a good *vaquero,*
now, a good rider and strong, and everyone likes him because
settlers have come in since then and taken land around here. Only
he doesn't make friends. He looks at the sea too much, too long. I
do not know what he thinks about; that's the only thing I do not
like about him.

I am very old, now, very old. I can hardly get on a horse. And
I am tired, tired of everything, just tired. Sometimes I wish that
eagle who protects me would forget me and let me join my
people.

La Costa del Sur

La Costa del Sur is simply a fragment found among de Angulo's papers and was published for the first time in the earlier Turtle Island edition of *Coyote's Bones*. The piece was written in the early forties, just after the author had left the Big Sur country for the final time.

La Costa del Sur

It was Sam Seward who first told me about the Big Sur country. Sam taught English and literature at Stanford. He had just returned from a ten-day hike on foot from Monterey in the north to San Luis Obispo in the south. "You never saw such a landscape!" he had said, "I did not imagine it was possible . . . like a dreamland, somewhere, not real. . . . Imagine: only a trail, for a hundred miles, bordering the ocean, but suspended above it a thousand feet, clinging half-way up the side of the sea-wall, and that wall at an incredible angle of forty-five degrees, a green wall of grass (he had seen it in winter—throughout the summer the green is brown-yellow) and canyons with oaks, redwoods, pines, mad-

ronyos, bluejays, quail, deer, and to one side the blue ocean
stretching away to China, and over all that an intense blue sky
with eagles and vultures floating about . . . and nobody, no humans there, solitude, solitude, for miles and miles—why! in one
place I walked thirty miles between one ranch and the next—what
a wilderness, what beauty, it's a dreamland—you must go
there. . . ."

I somewhat discounted the lyricism of a professional liter-
ateur (although I found it subsequently to be all of what Sam had
promised, and more!), still my curiosity was aroused, all the more
so because I was looking for a place in the country to settle and
raise cattle and horses.

I said to Sam: "Why should the country have remained so
wild?" "I think it is because when the first expedition was sent out
of Mexico with Portola to rediscover Monterey, they traveled
along the sea-shore all the way up to San Luis Obispo, and a little
beyond; well, there were about a hundred Spaniards and Indians
and two or three hundred horses and pack-animals—quite an expedition to tackle a totally unknown country without roads or
even trails! . . . and I imagine when they got into that tangle and
labyrinth of mountains that fall plumb into the ocean without
even a beach, they just got discouraged, and tried going around
that clump of mountains; they turned east away from the sea, and
found the Salinas Valley which led them ultimately to Monterey.
That first trip of Portola established the route for the Camino
Real and the Missions. Then Monterey became the capital of
California Alta and the center of development—and as there was
plenty of good flat land around it, north and west, nobody
bothered with that rough land to the south."

Sam was right. That is why that country was always known
to the *paisanos* of Monterey as "la costa del Sur," the coast to the
south; a wild, little known land, with two rivers; and these two
rivers, naturally, were known as "los rios al sur," the rivers to the
south—and to distinguish them: sur grande and sur chico, the little river to the south and the big river to the south. Then came the

Gringos, and that not very felicitous combination of "Big Sur." We still receive an occasional letter addressed to "Big Sewer"!

But to go back to my story. It was around Christmas time of '15, and I was loafing in Carmel (which at that time was not much more than two score houses or so); and one day, as I was riding my horse along the road, I saw two vaqueros on horseback. But these two were real vaqueros, and dressed up for going to town—nothing fancy or clownish, but the real old stuff: angora chaps, big rowel spurs that tinkled with the gait of the horse, wide sombreros (but not ridiculous); they were riding half-broken colts with jáquimas and fine horsehair mecates . . . and were they good-looking, the whole outfit of them, horses, men, and equipment!

Since they were paisanos I needed no introduction and I stopped them: "Where do you come from?" "Alla, de la costa del Sur, Allá lojos al diablo . . . from the coast to the south, from down there to the devil . . . we are on our way to town to spend Christmas with our mother." "Is there free land down there?" "Plenty of it, hermano, but too wild, too steep, too far from everywhere . . . nothing but coyotes and deer . . ." "Fine!" I said, "that's just what I am looking for . . . Will you take me down there, when you go back?"

And that's how I made the acquaintance of El Mocho, as we used to call him (like so many vaqueros he had lost a thumb in the coils of the reata), the best horse-breaker I ever knew, and the most reckless, dare-devil plenipotentiary whose laughter could be heard half-a-mile away.

He called for me, a week or so later, one morning, on horseback. And although we started early we did not reach his home, at the very end of the wagon-road, until nightfall. Nowadays, when you average sixty miles an hour on smooth highways, people do not realize what traveling horseback meant. A horse does not walk much faster than a man; I must have owned some hundred and fifty horses in my time—and I can only remember three who averaged a steady six-mile an hour walking gait under the saddle.

Such a horse is a benediction on a long trip; you are carried along
in bliss. But take a slow poke of a horse under you; you keep
urging him, urging him, urging him—at the end of the day you
are worn out! I should say that most horses average four miles an
hour at a steady walk.

That was the end of the wagon-road. The next morning we
started on the TRAIL! I shall never forget my first impression
when I saw that Coast. I was aghast. I stood still. I looked and
looked. What a panorama. The coast made a gentle curve so that I
was able to see it for all of thirty miles or so—a wall of green rising abruptly out of the sea, not really perpendicular but halfway
so. Headland succeeded headland, like the wings on a stage. And
along that wall, a thousand feet above the ocean, the trail.

"Well, what are you waiting for? Are you bemused? Encan-
tado?"

"Yes . . . estoy emocionado . . . que hermosura! . . . yes, this is
the country I was looking for."

"Wait, you haven't seen anything yet. Wait until I show you
the place I have in mind for you."

So we started again on the trail. But I was not used to such
height and I felt dizzy. I had to get off my horse and lead him. We
came to a bad place: there had been a slide, there was practically
no trail left. But the Mocho never got off his colt. Then the colt
lost his footing, went off the trail, and started to plunge down
that slide of loose rocks . . . My heart was in my mouth . . . In all
the years I have spent around cowboy camps and horse-ranches, I
have never seen a rider like this Mocho . . . he was off the saddle
like lightning, the colt turned a somersault and started to roll
down toward the ocean, and the Mocho leaping twenty feet at a
time, after him . . . he managed somehow to get hold of the
horse's head by the jáquima and keep him from turning over
again. Then they scrambled back to the trail, and went on.

After some riding we arrived at a cabin and dismounted.
That's where I first met Clarence, ex-Mormon, not much over
5-foot but strong as an ox, with the flat voice of the nearly deaf, a

little wizened face and a heart of gold—but alas, a rather inconsequential type of mind. He wasn't really a moron; it was rather that his mind did not follow the usual grooves and patterns. He came to live with me later on, and I got to know him quite well and appreciate his intimate knowledge of wild nature. He could make a lot of trouble, though, due to a complete ignorance of the cussedness of human nature—with charming naivete and the best intentions, coupled with a penchant for repeating tales, he finally succeeded in getting the whole Coast embroiled in a mix-up of feuds and counter-feuds that lasted twenty-five years—but that's another story, as the fellow said.

Clarence lived there all alone with a pet pig whom he had trained to sit on a chair at table. He also kept bees. He showed us a small churn he had just made out of a 3-lb. can of lard and a few sticks whittled with a pocket-knife. His butter was excellent. We had a cup of coffee with him, and remounted our horses.

We followed the County Trail again for two or three hours. Hanging on the mountainside, a thousand feet above the ocean, then dipping into a wooded canyon with giant redwoods, oaks, madronyos, maples (maples); I was struck by the diversity of trees; then out again onto grasslands, the trail curving around these "knees of the gods"; then in again into the next canyon. . . . in, out . . . in, out . . .

At last the Mocho said: "Here we go up to the place I have in mind for you to homestead" (he said *esquatar*—a barbaric neologism, from squatter, to squat!!). So we turned off the County Trail and started straight up the mountainside . . . and I must confess I got dizzy and had to get off my horse and lead him, much to the Mocho's amusement. Another hour's climb, and we were there, sixteen hundred feet above the ocean . . . but I mean above the ocean—the ocean, the blue Pacific, was there, practically under us (not more than a rifle-shot away), sixteen hundred feet below . . . and gulls flying, and we looking down on them so far down that they were the size of white pigeons.

What a scene! Yes, I lost my heart to it, right there and then.

This is the place for a freedom loving anarchist. There will never be a road into this wilderness . . . it's impossible! Alas, nothing is impossible to modern man and his infernal progress: they came with bulldozers and tractors before very long, and raped the virgin. Roads and automobiles, greasy lunch-papers and beer-cans, and their masters. And the shy Masters of the Wilderness receded to the depths of the canyadas, and back over the Ridge, into the yet unraped country of the Forest Reserve—But even there they are not safe; the well-meaning Rangers (boy-scouts of the forest, one good deed a day) are opening trails, and "restricted" camping grounds, and you must not smoke or swear. A Guide Book to the Wilderness, complete with figures and estimates! Lo, the untamed, adieu. . . .

II: LATER WORKS

Don Gregorio

On the recommendation of Ezra Pound, Peter Russell first published these *Don Gregorio* sketches in his magazine *Nine* back in the early fifties. Little need be said concerning these charming pieces, save that *Don Gregorio* resembles here rather intriguingly that other earlier *Don,* and that we find here also some possible source for those remarkable eccentricities which helped to define Mister de Angulo's very own character.

Don Gregorio
and the Straw Hat

That summer we were vacationing in Trouville, which in those days of the mid-90's was a fashionable seaside resort. My father's current fad at that time was the *Kneip Cure,* which enjoyed a great vogue in those days among the devotees of health and rational living. One of the tenets of the Cure was to eat slowly and chew the food thoroly—in fact you shud masticate every morsel no less than a dozen times before swallowing it. My father took this, as everything else, literally; there he sat at his meal, with his head turned sideways to the open book of the moment, conscientiously masticating each piece *twelve* times. He ate alone, and his meal lasted from five to seven o'clock. The rest of the family, my mother, my sister, my brother and i, trooped in at six o'clock and were finished by half past six. My father was never able to make any of us masticate properly, altho he tried.

Another tenet of the Cure was to walk *barefoot* in the grass before the morning dew had evaporated. This, my father did every morning. Both he and i were early risers, always up at dawn (i was about six or seven, then). So we sallied forth, both barefoot, and walked a mile or so out of town to where there were some lush green cow pastures, he walking ahead with his long strides and i trotting behind like a faithful dog.

My father never wore a hat. In those days a hat was as necessary a part of a man's costume as were his trousers, and to go about bareheaded was as unusual as to go about without his pants, and almost as shocking. But my father cared not a fig for public opinion (to which he referred, comtemptuously, as *la vanidad mundana*); he did not affront it; he did not ignore it; he simply did not see it. He never realized that he was an odd, an eccentric character. But my poor mother did! Doña Ysabel was a paragon of conventional correction (or maybe we thot so because of the contrast with Don Gregorio?).

That summer, however, my father was much bothered by the glare of sunlight; and on that particular morning, as we were returning on bare feet from those dewey meadows, he made an important decision: he wud buy a straw hat!

So, we turned into the town in quest of a hat-shop. The morning was just getting along and people were leisurely shopping here and there. We found a hat shop and went in. There was a demoiselle behind the counter and my father explained in his grammatically correct but atrociously pronounced French that he desired a straw hat with a very wide brim. The demoiselle smiled and said "Oui, Monsieur, certainement" and disappeared and soon returned with several trim *canotiers,* those stiff little hats they used to wear in summer in Europe and in New York but i never saw one in the West. My father's face fell. No, no, no, he cried, that was not at all what he wanted (and indeed, he wud have been a figure of fun in one of the little monkey hats, he with his prophet's face and flowing beard!). He wanted a hat with a large brim, a very wide brim.

So the demoiselle went back and returned with some more canotiers . . . the brim of these was surely all of a quarter-inch broader, in fact they were daringly wide brimmed. . . . Just then, my father's eye lit on a pile of gardener's hats put away on a top shelf. "Ha!" he exclaimed triumphantly, that was what he wanted.

The demoiselle's eyes were wide with horror. "Mais, Monsieur, ce sont des chapeaux de jardinier!" (Now, observe: she said they were gardener's hats, not garden hats. A tremendous difference in social classification!) My father's answer was, "It is all equal to me! I want one of those hats! Give me one of those hats!" She climbed on a short ladder and she brot them down. I thot she was going to burst into tears. As a final plea to my father to be reasonable, she said: "But Sir, they cost only six pennies." "Eh bien, tant mieux! all the better!" said my father, and he crowned himself with a gardener's hat. He really did not look bad at all in it. It fitted his noble face. The demoiselle's look of on-the-verge of tears changed to a slightly admiring one. But my father's eternal utilitarianism had to spoil the picture again. He demanded to have ribbons sewed on to the hat so he cud tie them under his chin against the wind. Now the demoiselle's smile changed to plain laughter. She rummaged under the counter and produced scissors, needle and thread, and a wide red ribbon. In a few deft movements she had two ribbons sewed on to the hat; my father crowned himself again; and she herself tied the scarlet bow-knot under his beard. She was laughing. Her laughter did not at all annoy my father. He simply remarked to me: "Pero, que amable es!" And we sallied forth into the street, my father barefoot and with his new hat, and me trotting behind him.

We were now going home, and there were quite a few people on the streets. Just then, coming in our direction, but on the other side of the street, we saw my mother. Doña Ysabel was short and somewhat corpulent; tightly laced in her corsets and wearing very high heels; she always dressed carefully in the correct mode of the day, but without any ostentation. So there she came as usual walking very erect with her short steps, holding her train in one hand and her parasol in the other. As i said, we saw her; *and she saw us at the very same instant.* She stopped abruptly for perhaps five seconds. Then she whirled around, and fled up the street.

"Ysabel! Eh . . . YSABEL!!" my father yelled in stentorian tones, taking long strides.

Passers-by stopped and turned around, staring, and shop-keepers came to their doorsteps. "Ysabel, Eh, Ysa-BEL!!" But Doña Ysabel was fleeing up the street, almost at a run. At the corner she turned into another street. My father stopped. He turned to me. "Pero, que le pasa, esta loco (what is the matter with her? is she crazy?)."

Don Gregorio's Bandoleer

My father hated pockets. He said they were illogical (why? asked my mother, and he answered: you don't understand) and unsightly, and they deformed the clothes (that from him!) and bulky (but why do you have to carry a department store along with you? you don't need all that truck, tantas cositas!). So he had his tailor make him special clothes *without* pockets, and he carried all his cositas in a bandoleer. Women do the same nowadays, but when i was a child, women used neither bandoleer nor handbag, nor did they have pockets to their clothes (except a dissimulated placket situated in the slit of the skirt, just beneath the bustle—and of course quite invisible since in walking a lady gathered her train in her right hand and held it off the ground by bunching it under her posterior).

In that placket she carried her money-purse. Her handkerchief she carried in her sleeve. That's all a lady need carry in those days (i haven't mentioned the umbrella, or parasol—according to the weather of the day—held in the left hand, but it goes without saying it). In those days only the prostitutes painted their faces or lips, or a few old ladies who had been known for their beauty when they were young, and now they couldn't accept their fate. At most it was permissible, and only in a woman "entre deux ages," to powder her face (but very lightly, just enough to hide the lines)—and perhaps, perhaps to do something to her eyes, but so carefully, so well, that it defied detection. Anything more was "maquillage" and only for the cocottes. As for a woman to make her face in the public eye—as they do now in restaurant, street-car, anywhere—it wud have been as shocking as if she had lifted her skirts to squat, or almost.

Now, in that bandoleer he carried an assortment of things, to-wit:

1.   3 pairs of spectacles: one for near vision, one for far vision, and one that combined both far and near.

2.   a pencil.

3.   his "breviary," for my father who was very pious, read the holy offices every day, like an ordained priest.

4.   his rosary beads.

5.   a bunch of slips of paper on which was printed his name and address; these he collected by cutting out the paper-band or wrapper around the newspaper to which he subscribed. My father considered calling cards one of the "mundane vanities." Anyway, Don Gregorio was one of those people who are called penny-wise and pound-foolish. He saved every piece of string, carefully rolling it up like a diminutive reata, and storing it away in a drawer.

Likewise he opened envelopes and saved them for scribbling paper. (But when we went to the country for the summer vacation, we travelled in a private railroad car! And that's how he went through the million or so in francs that belonged to my mother in about twenty years time and was practically a pauper in his old age. Don Gregorio, Don Gregorio de las Cositas, we used to call him, penny-wise and pound-foolish, so logical and so naive. He was quite unlike anybody i ever knew . . . but to come back to the cositas in that bandoleer:

6. his money-purse.

7. a pen-knife.

8. a compass (what for, in Paris?).

9. his second chronometer (i mean the no. 2 pocket-chronometer; the ship-chronometer of course never left the house!).

10. four handkerchiefs, big handkerchiefs, in colored plaids, like glorified bandannas, but of linen (glorious things, but you can't get any such things any more). One of these four handkerchiefs was for nose-blowing (altho Don G. almost never blew his nose. "I have no secretions!" he said proudly). The second handkerchief was for wiping his spectacles. The third kerchief was for opening doors when out of the house (Don Gregorio had caught the microbe phobia—this was not so very long after Pasteur and Metchnikoff, and microbes were the current fad—those terrible MICROBES of my childhood! Los microbios, los microbios! Alli vienen los Moros! . . .). As for the 4th and ultimate handkerchief, we never learned its use or purpose. When questioned about it, Don Gr. wud never answer, but merely smiled, as if to say: "Este es mi secreto!"

Don Gregorio
at the Bon Marché

My father cud at times turn into quite an orator, and this was all
the more surprising in a man ordinarily so silent. Unfortunately,
his gifts of oratory were usually spent on us children. We wud be
summoned into the presence by our rings. . . .

But I must explain about the rings. When Don Gregorio
wanted to communicate with his family, he rang (if we were at the
time in our Paris apartment; but in our country-house he used a
whistle, like a boatswain on board ship). For Dona Ysabel the
signal was two long rings; for my sister Pura, one long and one
short; for Manuel, one long and two shorts, and for myself one
short and two longs. So, when we heard rrrrring-ring, then

rrrrrrring-ring-ring, and then rrrrring-ring-ring-ring it was like a
general alarm, and we knew we were in for a lecture. We wud
troop into Don Gregorio's cabinet-de-travail and stand in a row
in front of his desk where he sat reading a book, or perhaps writing, and we waited for his clearing-of-the-throat. This was akin to
the regulation three knocks that preceded the raising of the cur-
tain on the stage. Hrmmm, hrmmm, hrmmm. . . . Then he wud
rise and stand up on his chaufferette, that foot-warmer—a flat box
with a copper lid and a little wick oil-lamp inside—which he carried around with him all over the place everywhere in the apartment because his feet were always cold; and that made him stand a
little over six feet. Now he plunged into the exordium. It might
start something like this: "Hrmmm, hrmmm, hrmmm. . . . Order
is a great quality. It is perhaps the greatest gift from God to man.
Without order, the world is nothing but a hodge-podge (sin
orden, el mundo no es mas que una sinrazon). With order . . ."
and so on and so forth, thru the main body of the discourse to the
final peroration . . . to the final peroration, that is, *if* no accident
occurred. Jaime was usually the accident because as a child he was
tempestuous and impatient, and he might break out with: "Yes, i
know, it's that blue pencil i took out of the drawer (the second
drawer on my father's bureau, on the right hand, where he kept
colored pencils and saved-up little rolls of string), but I'll go and
fetch it . . ." then my father wud give me a withering glance (and
his blue eyes cud be very piercing, at times), and with great dignity, but without any heat, he said: "Silencio! . . . *Vuelvo a repetir*"
and he wud start again at the very beginning; "Order is a great
quality; it is perhaps the greatest . . ." and so on and so forth.
How ever many times interrupted he never lost his temper, but
only said "Silencio! . . . Vuelvo a repetir!" and start all over again.
There was only one exception. Sometimes we wud be seized by an
acces de fou rire, that hysterical laughter without reason. On such
occasions my father did not start again at the very beginning. He
merely sat down, took up his book, and waited for composure to
return to us. Then he wud get up, stand on his chaufferette and

resume the lecture at the very point where he had left off, and continue till the end of the peroration.

But i was going to tell about Don Gregorio and the Bon Marché. In those days of my childhood the Louvre and the Bon Marché were the two great department stores. In those stores the system of making purchases was thoroly French and complicated. With the help of a clerk you selected your article, but you didn't pay him for it; he gave you a slip and armed with this slip you went to the comptoir, and took your place in the queue. Then when your turn came to appear before another clerk who sat at the comptoir behind a grille, you presented your slip, paid for the purchase, and received another slip which you presented at the delivery counter where you received your purchase, in case you wanted to take it home with you—but if you wanted it to be delivered at your house, then you said: "a domicile," and gave your name and address to the clerk.

But my father always had trouble with his name and address, because of his foreign accent. So he always carried a provision of those bands that are used in France to wrap around your newspaper. Your name and address are printed on them. As Don G. wud not countenance calling-cards (because he considered them a mundane vanity) he carefully—but several years later he relented. Then he had large bristol-boards, four inches square, engraved ("at least," he said, "if i want to write a message, i will have enough space") he had several thousand of these engraved, for "reasons of economy"; they were of three kinds: Monsieur de Angulo, Madame de Angulo, and Monsieur et Madame de Angulo. The second kind my mother carefully hid, then threw away; the third kind, my father cud never again find, in spite of all his searching thru the drawers of his bureau, but i don't think my mother threw those away—i think she merely misplaced them very carefully—he carefully cut out those bands, and saved them, and carried a little stack of them in his bandolier. Then when he had to furnish his name-and-address to any one, he wud gravely dig into the bandolier, and hand over the wrap band cut from the newspaper-wrap. He did this with great dignity, even a sort of flourish, while my mother hovered in the vicinity, and pretended not to know him (we children did not care, rather enjoyed it).

Usually it worked, and the clerk merely scribbled the information on his blotter.

But on this occasion, it did not work as usual.

The clerk was a man with a sallow complexion, a very sallow complexion indeed. When he asked the stereotyped question: "votnoeadres" my father handed him one of the slips. The clerk gave it a passing glance, then threw back the original question at my father. My father did not answer. He merely stuck the slip right under the nose of the clerk. The clerk pushed it aside, and fairly shouted at my father "Kekseksbout-de-papier? J'vous demande vot' nom-et-adresse."

Then the homily started. My mother was pretending to look at some articles on a counter, but her face was red as a tomato. The clerk's complexion had turned from sallow to livid. Customers were staring. A floor-walker tried to intervene but my father said to him a formidable "Silencio." We children were enjoying ourselves hugely. We had been thru so many of these orations!

This time the lecture was all about the rights of the public and the good sense for business to show unfailing courtesy to the customer—a theory generally accepted in America, but not prevalent in France.

The peroration, however, i regret to say, was marred by a touch of argumentum ad hominem. Don Gregorio had finished; he let a slight pause elapse; then he added a postscript: "And anyhow, you are bilious, as anyone can see from your complexion." Unfortunately, like many Spaniards, Don G. got his b's and v's thoroly mixed, and what he said was: "Et d'ailleurs, bous etes Vilieux; cela se boit a botre teint!" Then he marched off, followed in procession by all of us, altho Doña Ysabel was lagging quite a distance behind.

Don Gregorio
and his Chronometer

My father had always had a passion for watches. Yes, a passion! not just an interest, but a passion. Shortly before his death when after 20 yrs. of estrangement I had decided it was stupid on my part to continue the feud, and went and made my submission he said: "I don't remember when this passion started . . . it must have been during my childhood . . . the idea that you could, so to speak, materialize time (that most immaterial thing) and metamorphose it into a maze of wheels inside a little box. . . ."

He kept his watches as other people keep a stable of horses. Usually, watch fanciers are interested in the face of the watch, its style, Ier. Empire, Restoration, Rococo, etc. They keep those watches under cloche and let them run down. Not so with Don Gregorio. He had about three score watches and *they all ran!* He kept them in a closet with shelves. If you were not forewarned and opened the door of the closet you almost fell over backward! Such a racket! Such a tintamarre! Sixty watches ticking at the same time!

Then, on every floor of our villa in La Baule there was one or two of those horloges bretonnes, 6 ft. tall. They had a pendulum and a couple of weights. You wound the weights every two weeks. Those were very ornamental clocks. But Don Gregorio did not care a rap about that. The looks of a clock did not interest him; what he wanted was that it shud give the time properly.

But the king of them all was THE chronometer. It was a marine chronometer, one of those things in a box about a foot square, and hung so that it was always level. It had been made by Leroy-Beaulieu, the great chronometer-maker of the Bould. de la Madeleine. Don Gregorio had paid a fortune for it! Naturally, you never changed it. You simply calculated each time the amount it had gained or lost. A good chronometer does not vary more than seven seconds a day. But the really important thing is that it should vary (either advance or retard) a regular amount. A chronometer which gains a second one day, then three the next, then retards one second the next day, is not a good chronometer; too temperamental!

In those days before wireless, my father got the *right* time from the Navy, at Saint-Nazaire some 20 kilometers from La Baule. My father made the trip every 2 weeks, by train, just to obtain the right time. He carried in his sack a small quasi-chronometer and this he put in accord with the Chronomètre de la Marine. He always went alone except that I accompanied him. I adored my father the way one adores God. If I had had my way I wud never have left his side. He never even noticed my presence, and he never said anything to me. He was one of the most silent men I have ever known; at least in those days he was.

I pause here for a moment for a query: *why* was Don G. so

much in love with watches? As I have said already, it was not the artistic value of the watch; that left him completely indifferent. Neither was it the *collector's instinct*. My father collected many items that usually go into collections; at various times he collected lenses, pictures, rocks, meterorites (that was when we were in the Pyrénées—and the peasants, the montagnards, collected them in the high mountains and then sold them to the tourists—but always after breaking them in half to show the beautiful shining structure of the metal—to my father this was sacrilege! he wud buy none of those, to the amazement of the peasants—he tried vainly to explain to them that these ugly objects came *from another planet than* the earth, they came from outer space—mais vas donc leur faire comprendre, ces pauvres imbéciles! They looked at my father with suspicion). He collected moorish plates. Postage-stamps are the only thing he never collected, strangely enuf! So, Don Gregorio *did* have the instinct of a collector, there is no denying it. Yet i was certain, even far back in the days of my childhood that the collector's instinct had nothing to do with it. I was puzzled—and I did not understand it until years later, just before his death.

So i quarreled with him and came to America and had no more communication with him until years later when i realized that i was acting like a fool and went back and made my submission, and he died happy.

Now, the story of my father, his valet-de-chambre and the chronometer happened some ten years later, during the First World War. (I volunteered in the medical corps, 1st Lieut. and spent the next 18 months trying to find out *where i was supposed to be!* The Army had misplaced my papers. It's incredible but it is so!) So, i never was present at the "Affaire du Chronomètre." All I know is what my sister told me.

Altho my father hardly ever spoke to anyone his figure was well-known in the country-side where he took long rides on his bicycle. They thot he was a sort of madman, but quite harmless. "Le millionaire espagnol" they called him. Somehow or other the idea had entered his head that he had been appointed official timekeeper for the county. He had taken it upon himself to care for the great church clock on the main square of the town. He had also taken charge of the clock at the railway-station. And whenever he met someone in uniform, the postman maybe, or a garde-champêtre, he offered to give them the correct time. The transaction was a silent one—no words wasted. Don Gregorio took his watch out of his pocket and the other person did the same. They compared the watches side-by-side; the small error, if there was one, was corrected and each man went his way, smiling.

All this was before the days of the radio. The radio changed Don Gregorio's life. No longer necessary, those bi-weekly trips to Saint Nazaire to get the proper time at the Bureau de la Marine. Now he cud have the correct time *twice* a day, at noon and at midnight. Incredible! Life was good.

The war! and the American troops occupied Brittany and went joyously at the game of teaching the Frogs the ways of the superior life. All private radios were, of course, ordered dismantled. But now that he had tasted the intoxication thing, he cud not face going back to the old life. *He decided to take a chance!* He would keep his antenna. Nobody wud notice. The childish lack of appreciation of reality is appalling! It also showed an appalling lack of understanding of war and the military mind. Because he was so certain of his honesty he thot that honesty wud immediately become apparent to the others. My sister was in tears!

It did not take the occupying Americans long to discover my father's radio, and they demanded Don Gregorio's arrest as a spy. In vain did the French authorities plead with the American commander. "The man is well-known to us—absolutely harmless— just a crackpot—." The American was obdurate.

Now things began to move fast—everybody moved fast except Don Gregorio. He was sublimely ignorant of the danger. He had done no wrong, he was quite serene. But it was the hour of his lunch when they came to arrest him, and he refused to move until he had had his lunch. In vain the Commissaire de Police appealed to him, "Monsieur, je vous en prie, pressez-vous, pressez-vous, vous n'avez pas l'air de comprendre la situation. Vous entendez ces cris, dehors? Eh bien c'est la foule en émeute. Vous n'avez probablement jamais vu une foule en émeute. Moi, c'est mon métier. Ce sont de braves gens qui tout à coup deviennent des bêtes-en-fureur."

My sister told me that it was one of the most terrible moments of her life. "Figurez-vous cetter foule, d'ordinaire de bons paysans, des commerçants polis, des voisins aimables. Et tous hurlaient 'A mort l'espion! L'espagnol à la lanterne, l'espagnol à la lanterne!' And between them and the grille of the garden, some twenty mounted policemen with slung carbines. In the salle-à-manger Don Gregorio eating an omelette with perfect unconcern, served by the butler in civvies (they had arrested him as accomplice)."

Finally the omelette was finished and the three of them descended the stairs and entered the police wagon. The mounted policemen quickly formed an escort around the wagon, and off they went for the railroad station. The way led past the Place de l'Eglise. The Commissaire told my sister that Don Gregorio begged them to stop so he cud put the big clock on time.

The Americans kept Don Gregorio and the butler in jail for a whole month before they were convinced of his innocence. Don Gregorio and the butler had to share the same cell. Don Gregorio kept up a jeremiad of self-accusatory acts of contrition. It was God punishing him, and that sort of thing. Eugène at first assented "Oui Monsieur, oui monsieur." Then he became surly and did not open his mouth any more. Then one day, in the midst of a jeremiad he got up deliberately from his cot, he bent over and took hold of the pot-de-chambre in both hands, and he stood over Don Gregorio: "Un mot de plus . . . et je vous mets la tête en bouillie!" My father yelled: "Au secours. Il est devenu fou!" After that they were put in two separate cells.

Years later, when I visited him and my sister, i found them in the Basque country, on the French side. He had changed very much, of course, mellowed. My sister explained to me that she could not bear living in La Baule after the trouble. The place has become odious to her. "Je n'oublierai jamais le cauchemar de cette foule hurlant 'A mort l'espion! l'espagnol à la lanterne!' Ces têtes défigurées par la cruauté, par une passion obscène!" She had sold the house for a song and they had come here to the lovely pays basque.

One evening, my father and I sat outside smoking. The night was warm and clear, and the stars brilliant. My father began telling me how he had managed to get the right time before private radios were allowed again. He had made friends with one of the French priests at a local astronomical observatory. He had learned to calculate "sidereal time" by making observations on the stars. And with emotion choking his voice he told me how he had discovered a new world! "Just think, just think about the speed of light, 200,000 kilometers per second!" His voice had dropped to a murmur. He began to tell me about the wonders of modern physics. Then he told he how time was only one of the four coordinates of matter. . . . *Then it was that I understood his passion for watches.*

The night-chill entered into us and we went indoors. It was almost midnight and time for the broadcast of the time from the Eiffel tower. And while we waited for it a strange expression came over his face. "They* wanted me to study law! I never under stood the law! For me it was only a jumble of illogicalities, a senseless galimatias! Just suppose they had let me learn physics and chemistry, biology—I might have become a great scientist! But Spain is a barbarous country!" and while he was saying that, a wave of bitterness was swelling inside myself. I wanted to say: "Yes, and you my father kept me in schools of Jesuits where we were forbidden to read books on physics and chemistry, and biology!" but I did not say it.

Pretty soon the signals began coming in. The large room was

---

*By "they" he meant the Jesuits. He had been one of their brilliant pupils.

very dimly lit by an oil-lamp, one of those things in the Pyrénées
that have not changed since Roman times. You still find them in
use. It looks like half of an avocado pear, with a wick which dips
in the oil (olive oil was so cheap in those days!). The wick hangs
outside, and it gives out a soft yellow light. The room was full of
dancing shadows.

Now the signals were coming fast and Don G. was entering
them in notebooks for the several chronometers (of the 2nd
class), and to his horror one of them that he was especially interested in had gone on a rampage! It was several seconds off (we
discovered the next day that it was my father who had made a
mistake!).

I started for my room and turned around to say good-night.
My father was sitting in his chair, a picture of desolation. He held
the chronometer in his hand and was shaking his head slowly,
from side to side. He was saying in an injured tone: "Ay, tu, bribon! bribon!" (oh, you, scoundrel, scoundrel!).

"Marceline, Vous Etes Une Cochonne!"

For some reason my mother nursed me herself. Just the same, when i was born they sent for a nurse, a "dry nurse." This was Marceline, and she stayed with us until i was six, when she went back to her "pays"; she came from central France.

Marceline was a typical peasant: obdurate, stupid, slow (my father nicknamed her Culo-do-Plomo). Naturally she became devoted to me and i became devoted to her. In a sense, she was "mother" to me much more than my mother. Yet, note this point: she addressed me as "Monsieur Jaime," never as plain Jaime; and of course, she used the "Vous."

I can see us going out after lunch, my sister aged 9, my

brother 7, and myself 4, all in charge of Marceline. We go up the Champs-Elysees, around the Arc-de-Triomphe, then we enter the Avenue du Bois (de Boulogne), and before we have gone very far we find some of our "gang" (my sister and my brother are always the leaders, everywhere, it is they who organize games); i hate children, so i stay with "Culo-do-Plomo" who had joined the other bonnes d'enfants on a bench, i play by myself making sand-pies.

Now, for a long time i had been wondering about the jets d'eau of the Place de la Concorde. *What made the water go up?* i used to wonder and wonder and wonder. i lay in bed at night imagining a complicated system of paddle wheels each one throwing some water up to the paddle above, and so on and on. But i knew intuitively that there was something simpler than that!

i asked Marceline. She said she did not know. i insisted that she did. "Tell me, tell me! i want you to tell me!!" I got myself into a fury. i stamped my foot. I yelled "Marceline, vous êtes une cochonne!!" to which she replied with calm: "Je le sais. Vous me l'avez dejà dit! . . . vous êtes une vieille cochonne!!"

How that problem of artesian water worried me.

It was 2 or 3 years later that i understood, partly. i was playing in the pantry. i had let the water half fill the sink and i was doing something with a little boat i had carved. i don't remember what it was that i was doing but it involved a long rubber tube. Anyway, at a certain moment i let the end of the tube drop; the tube had been full of water, and one end of it was still in the sink. i saw the water run out of the other end onto the floor of the pantry and i expected that all the water already inside the tube would thus run out, but to my amazement the water *continued* to run out . . . and more, and more . . . and more until *all* the water in the sink had been siphoned out!

We soon heard from the people in the apartment below: their ceiling was leaking! Hulaballoo!! the concierge was there in no time, and the servants from below, and my mother and my brother and my sister. They were all trying to find out from me what it was that i was trying to do. But i was like one in a trance! i knew confusedly in my mind that there was the answer to my great puzzle: what made the water go up. I cudn't work it out but somehow, intuitively, i knew that the two phenomena were connected, the jets d'eau of the Place de la Concorde and the water siphoned out of the sink.

I was angry, i felt cheated. Why didn't they explain important things to little boys?!!

Yes, i was angry, i thot to myself: "yes, at school you fill me up with stupid stories, with arguments about sin, about the state of grace, all sorts of things which bore me, things which I don't understand (and which, i suspect, you do not understand either)! Meanwhile you let a miracle, a real miracle, go by, and you do not tell me! A miracle which makes me dance with joy, the miracle of communicating vases, the miracle of water going up-hill! Either you have no imagination, or you are very stupid."

Yes, i was angry; i felt cheated; i felt they had let me down. And i wanted to shout: "Vous êtes des cochons! vous êtes des cochons!" i was around 8 or 9. i made my final rebellion when i was just turned 12. i remember that date because it was when i made my "first communion"—a gala day for most boys, but for me a day of disillusion, a day of bitterness. The whole thing, then, was a farce. i cud no longer believe my parents, my teachers. i was on my own; if there is a Truth then i must find it by myself—i was alone, and i was scared. Six long years of loneliness, of bitterness, of doubt—until i broke away and came to America.

The Lariat

The idea for *The Lariat* came to de Angulo upon reading a Bancroft edition of the diaries and journals of the early Mission priests of Spanish California. Upon the completion of *The Lariat,* and with reference to the author's *Don Bartolomeo,* written a good twenty years earlier, de Angulo began to imagine a trilogy of works devoted to the Spanish, Mexican and Anglo 'confrontation' with the traditional magical cosmologies of the Native American peoples of Northern California, a 'confrontation' which is realized in this particular text in part by the constantly shifting, radical, temporal and spatial 'point of view.' *The Lariat,* then, was seen by the author as the first, or 'Spanish' volume in this trilogy; the earlier *Don Bartolomeo* as the second, or 'Mexican' volume; and a final volume was begun, to center around the encounter between an early twentieth

century anthropologist and a beguiling, Native American medicine-
doctor, or (as was the proposed title for this volume) *The Witch*. A draft
of *The Witch* does indeed survive among de Angulo's papers but it is
clear from the size of this manuscript, no more than thirty pages, and its
compressed almost pidgin-English syntax, based rather restrictedly on
Achumawi grammatical precepts, that the author's best creative energies
had by then moved elsewhere, moved in fact into the composition of
Indians in Overalls, a text which fills out the ideal of this trilogy completely, if however in a wholly different literary form.

    The Lariat has been justifiably considered de Angulo's most difficult
work as its spatial movements seem almost twenty-first century and
quite oblique; and yet, perhaps for these very reasons, both de Angulo's
wife, Nancy Freeland de Angulo, and the poet Ezra Pound considered it
the author's finest achievement. It is also as close to a true autobiography
of Jaime de Angulo's spirit as ever we are liable to have.

The Lariat

Beware, white man, of playing with magic of the primitive. It may be strong medicine. It may kill you. Ye, sons and daughters, foster children of the cities, if ye would go to the wilderness in search of your Mother, be careful & circumspect, lest she lure you into her secret places, whence ye may not come back.

1
Fray Luis comes West to worst the Devil

Who was Fray Luis?

We do not really know. He had come from Old Spain, so much is clear. He may perhaps have been that second son of the Don Aniceto mentioned in a family record of the parish of Haro, and whose name was so curiously omitted by the scribe's oversight. The record reads:

... The second son of Don Aniceto after a turbulent youth was touched by the grace of God and entered holy orders. He took the habit of San Francis, and was sent to the Americas, to the missions of Alta California. Recognizing his indomitable energy, his superiors turned the adventurous spirit of the man to the greater glory of God, and thus it was that he travelled from one Mission to another along the Coast of the Pacific Ocean, entering the wild hills covered with forests to preach the Holy Doctrine to the savage Indians of the woods. Until the Devil, Father of all Malice, alarmed at his success, counselled their priests to kill him, and he was crowned with the glory of the martyrs. The third son of Don Aniceto, Don Jaime, studied in Salamanca . . .

But even if his name had not been so strangely omitted, we would still remain in doubt as to his identity, for like many friars of that time he was known only by his nom de religion: Fray Luis. Fray Luis he remains for us, may God rest his passionate soul!

Fray Luis came to Monterey in California, in the days of the Indians. He came to save their pagan souls, but as we shall see, he used the powers of sorcery, once, and lost his own.

We may find some excuse for his sin in the violence of the passion of a man surrendered to God, in his agony as the day drew near when he would be forced to witness the profanation, the rape of his own soul. For, was not that Indian girl part and parcel of his soul? He himself had redeemed her. He himself had instructed her in the true faith. He himself had poured the waters of baptism over her lovely head. . . . The water had trickled down her throat, and a drop ran between her breasts. They were full and goat-shaped, like most Indians', and he associated them vaguely in his mind with the aroma of chocolate scented with vanilla.

And now he must perform another sacrament, bind her to the object of her carnal desire, a handsome half-breed, a half-savage, a youth in whose eyes lurked the gleam of untamed passions. He must deliver his dove into such claws! It would have been better indeed to leave her a pagan. . . . To find one's soul revealed only to be forced to prostitute it, and in the very name of God's sacred ministry!

Let us be charitable and realize the enormous temptation for such a mind in its agony to clutch at a straw and turn for help to the very monsters he had come to destroy. The monsters helped him. They gave him their power. He used it. Then, in the terror of his repentance, he betrayed his new masters, he went back to his own God. But the monsters had hold of him by a rope. The monsters had hold of one end, and the other was girt around his loins. An unbreakable rope, a vaquero's reata, a monk's cord. . . .

Struggle, struggle, Fray Luis! the monsters are pulling, pulling, dragging you down . . . Ah! It is useless, Fray Luis. You gave them your soul. Down you go.

Who was Fray Luis? Who he was appears best from his own curious diary:

. . . Wednesday, Feast of San Fernando, Confessor and Martyr. I arrived here last night, at this Mission of San Carlos Borromeo del Carmelo, and very tired. Fray Bernardo is Superior of this Mission which is a very thriving one having been the pet of Fray Junipero, may his soul rest in Heaven. And it surely must, for he earned it, as does any one who comes here from the South by following the Coast. A more villainous country I have never seen. There are neither roads nor trails. I would have done better to come round-about by the Valley and Mission Soledad, but I tried to take a short cut and came directly along the Coast through the country of those wild Esselen Indians whom I hope so much to convert. But it was an infernal trip and my donkey agrees with me. I shall not be able to ride him for a week. And yet I walked a great deal of the time during the last four days, so much so that I wore out a new pair of sandals and the bottom of my cassock is in shreds. Usually during my journeys into the rough country I wrap it around my waist, it is so much easier to walk or ride, and I don't think that our father San Francis was dreaming of American Missions, we do enough penance in this wilderness, but this time it was worse penance yet, lacerating my bare legs with the thorns of the trail. I must either wrap my legs with strips of buckskin like some of these Indians or wear leather trousers like the vaqueros. That will shock that old maid of Fray Bernardo and he will send a long epistle to Mexico. Fussy old mollycoddle, trotting from one warehouse to another, he prays the mass of Saint Tallow, Saint Wool and Saint Corn. May he be granted as many days of indulgence as all the heads of cattle he has made the converts raise for the Church. That is enough in any case to send him straight to heaven, for the old eunuch knows not temptation and his only sins are those of old women . . . grumbling and avariciousness. Well, each one serves God according to his own talent, I tame wild horses and he makes them work. I wear out my sandals and tear my cassock and risk an arrow in the seat thereof or a more vital spot to bring the effulgent light of the true faith to these lost sheep sunk in the dark labyrinth of superstitious slavery. "Come, my brothers, the life is not in your trees and in your rocks, it is in Our Father, He who made us and all, the only God. See Him behind the tree, under the rock, all beauty, incandescent and terrible, lovely in the image of His Son. Come and adore the true God." But evidently I should amend it thus: "Come and work for Fray Bernardo of the Tallow." Fray Tallow! I will wrap my cassock around my waist, if I please, and wear boots and spurs, beautiful silver spurs, and a wide sombrero to save my tonsure from the sun, I'll tie a bright silk around my neck, I'll mount a wild stallion, I'll turn in the saddle and thumb my nose at you, I'll ride to the hills. . . . Father in Heaven, Jesus, Saint Fernando, Angel of my guard, come and save me! Chase this devil away! Scourge me, beat me! Oh, my God, why must thou always tempt me? Have pity! Has it not been enough? . . .

Fray Luis must have spent a night of remorse, for the next day he writes in a more chastened mood:

I spent the morning with Fray Bernardo, making the rounds of the Mission. We had to visit everything, the tallow works, the piles of hides, the granaries, the tile works and the adoberia. The good padre is very proud of it all, of the good order, of the prosperousness, of the apparent contentment of the Indians. They are working in their usual lazy way, and they smiled when we passed. Their eyes followed Fray Bernardo and I could see that they were fond of him. Well, he gives them plenty of atole, and he does not whip them much. This noon I tasted the pozole myself, and I found a lot of meat scraps in it, much more than we ever put in at San Antonio or at San Juan Capistrano or any of the other missions where I have stayed. No wonder the Indians here are so fat. And I didn't notice any of the sullen looks of San Antonio, nothing but that shadow of gentle sadness over their eyes. They all have it, these Indians, when they are away from their rancherias. Fray Bernardo talked and talked in his tight Catalonian accent. I think he comes from Mallorca or another one of the Balearic Islands. Anyway he is the most active old man I ever saw. Quite an administrator and very pious. But oh! so garrulous and such a child in some ways. For instance, he took me this afternoon to see the magnificent beach which is not far from the Mission. Well, there, just on the other side of the rocks, there was an Indian girl bathing and all naked. What a scolding she got from Fray Tallow! ". . . Didn't that hussy know that it was strictly against the rules? She would get the lash for that! Shameless wench, why didn't she go back among the gentiles? . . ." all of this in mixed Rumsen and Catalan. The poor little one was standing before us, with tears in her eyes, very much distressed at all the violence, but quite plainly not understanding a word of what he said. I questioned her in the language of Mission San Antonio where she came from. She said she belonged to a rancheria of Esselenes, back in the hills near the Coast between here and San Antonio, that she had only been here a week, that she did not understand the language of the Rumsen Indians, nor the language of the white men, why was this man so angry, was he a powerful sorcerer, and would I please ask him not to give her the evil eye. When I interpreted all this, Fray Bernardo tore his hair. "What? Another language yet? Misericordious Father in Heaven, how many languages are there in this California? I have been here all these years and I never heard of Helens before. And now who is going to instruct this poor wild girl?" I assured him that I would, since I knew the Sextapay language and this girl seemed to understand it. At this he was very much relieved, and we went home, he to his account-books and I to my worries. I am worried. I think that innocently I put an evil thought into that girl's heart. I need not have explained to her the cause of Brother Tallow's wrath. I should have invented some excuse. But my wits were asleep because I was struggling with the work of translation. At first she didn't understand. She looked at me incredulously. Then she seemed to comprehend, and she began to laugh, but she suddenly checked herself, and slowly the blush of shame crept all over her dark skin. And I who had been innocent of any thought up to this moment, felt myself blushing by contagion. Seeing this, the girl turned and fled toward the rocks where she had left her zarape.

At supper we had a visitor, a young vaquero, the son of a settler who lives way down the Coast. He was one of the leather-jacket soldiers in the first expedition with Captain Portola, and he deserted with several others who could not endure the arrogance and harshness of Lieutenant

Fages. Later they were amnestied, but this man had already taken a wife in the tribe where he took refuge, precisely the Esselen tribe of today's naked girl. He had already a son of two years when the news of the amnesty reached him in the rancheria of gentiles where he was living, with another deserter. His companion returned, but he chose to stay. Now he has a house down the Coast. He is getting old. His son, who was telling us all this story at supper, is a typical vaquero, tall and handsome, with the Indian blood in him showing only in his eyes and hair, and perhaps his temper, for after some courteous conversation he suddenly dropped into a sullen mood and became silent. Fray Bernardo says that he had never heard him speak so long before. It appears that he has been a frequent visitor at the Mission of late. Fray Bernardo likes him and encourages him to come for he thinks that he may perhaps use him to take care of the Mission cattle. There is a rule here imposed by the Military Authorities forbidding to let any Indian ride horseback. They seem to think that all the converts and neophytes would run away if they had a chance, but I say that it is no use to tie them here unless they are truly willing to stay in the service of the true God, and why not cut off their legs while we are at it! Tomorrow I intend to celebrate the Mass for the soul of that one who died seven years ago tomorrow through my fault. Ay, Dios de mis pecados!

2
And finds him entrenched in the Wilderness

On top of a ridge facing the Pacific Ocean, at dawn.

Silence everywhere, except for the confused murmur of the sea, three thousand feet below. The steep slopes facing the Occident are still in darkness. Here and there small bands of deer are grazing, moving about like shadows.

The sun rises, peeking over the top of the furthest ridge on the orient. A wild country is revealed, a maze of ridges and canyons filled with fog. The silence is broken. The birds twitter everywhere. The bluejays greet one another.

BLUEJAY: "Good morning, Sir. How did you spend the night?"

ANOTHER BLUEJAY: "Very well, thank you. What a fine morning isn't it? But I am afraid the day is going to be hot."

FIRST BLUEJAY: "I think that you are right. I like the hot weather, myself, but my wife suffers very much."

SECOND BLUEJAY: "Well, I am like you. I can stand any kind of weather, myself. It's all the same to me. But it's pretty hard on the little ones. My family is just beginning to fly."

FIRST BLUEJAY: "So is mine. And let me tell you, between us, I'll be glad when they are out on their own for good. All this worry . . . !"

SECOND BLUEJAY: "Yes, yes, a family is a great responsibility, a great responsibility . . . Say! Do look at that Magpie, will you? . . . Went by with her nose in the air and not even a good morning for civility! The hussy!"

FIRST BLUEJAY: "Oh, don't pay any attention to such people. . . . Excuse me a minute, I see a worm. . . . Here, have a bit of worm with me. . . . Don't mention it, nothing at all. And by the way, have you heard about a white man passing through here the other day?"

SECOND BLUEJAY: "Yes, I did. I didn't see him myself, but I have been told about it. First white man here in years and years, they say . . . except for that old fellow who has been living here ever since my grandfather was a little boy."

FIRST BLUEJAY: "Oh, he doesn't count! He is just like our Indian people. He is just like them . . . and his son even more so. But white men are different. At least that's what they say. They say you can't understand white people. They say you never can tell what they are going to do, that's what they say. About this white man, they tell me he went by here at nearly sundown, and that he split himself in two, once."

SECOND BLUEJAY: "What d'you mean, split himself in two? I didn't hear about that."

FIRST BLUEJAY: "Yes, split himself in two . . . that's what they tell me, and one half looked like a doe, with long ears, but it had a tail like a puma, and the other half had only two legs and no tail, like a wildcat, and the white man's head went with that. But I don't believe it, do you?"

SECOND BLUEJAY: "You can't tell! Don't you remember how we all got excited when our white man, that old fellow, came here? He did the same thing, and now you don't even think it's strange."

FIRST BLUEJAY: "Yes, that's quite true. Well, I wonder what it all means. My grandfather says there must be something wrong about so many white men coming into this country. But you know how old folks are! They don't like anything new. Now, these two here, this old man and his son, they have been here for a long time, and yet they have never done us any harm."

A BIG BUCK who has been scratching his hide against the bark of a pine-tree: "They don't do me and my people as much harm as our own Indians!"

A LITTLE FOX: "Oh, I would love to see a white man, a real white man!"

AN OLD FOX: "Keep quiet, you little fool! You don't know what you are talking about! You are just like that old brainless buck. He ought to know better! My friends, let me tell you, I used to live way up north from here, where there is a river emptying into the sea. Then lots of white men came there, not just two, but many of them. And I saw the white men kill so many of my relatives that I moved down here. They use a special kind of bow and arrows. It makes Pum! and you have no time to dodge. If they ever come here it will be our end! But I don't think they will ever come so far . . ."

THE TWO BLUEJAYS: "Tschak! tschak! tschak! Run everybody, all of us! I see two Indians coming this way along the ridge!"

The deer leap down the slope, crashing through the brush. The foxes slink away. Silence again. Way down below, the ocean is sparkling and stretches away, away to the end of the sky. A maze of ridges and hillsides covered with chaparral, already beginning to dance in the heat of early morning.

Halfway down the slope, a little flat, with a few Indian huts, and a small house of logs and adobe, with a chimney. Smoke rises from the chimney. Below, a condor is soaring around and around. The sun shines on his back and wings at times. Hundreds of feet below him, near the water, sea-gulls are specks of white against the blue.

Not a sail on the Ocean. Silence. Silence. Immensity. Every little while, a puff of breeze brings the faint din of the roar of the breakers.

"Father, there is a new friar at the Mission."

"Ah . . . Give me another piece of meat, boy. That's tender meat! Your cousin brought it yesterday. He takes good care of me while you are away. . . . He said he saw some cattle below the Spring of the Madronyo. You had better ride there this morning. They'll be drifting into the back hills soon, and get wild again."

"All right. I'll go. . . . This monk is tall and lean. He does not speak like Fray Bernardo. He speaks more like you."

"Maybe he comes from Castilla. . . . You had better take the sorrel colt. He needs a ride."

"You mean I need to be bucked off?" the young man laughed. His teeth were white. His skin was very dark. He tore into another piece of venison. Then he spoke again, his mouth full:

"I don't like his manners. He is polite enough . . . but he is not friendly, like Fray Bernardo."

"Lots of people are like that, son, in my country. It does not signify. It's just their manner. . . . I think it's going to rain soon. . . . And your cousin says that a bear killed another cow."

"Bear, fiddlesticks! A bear with bow and arrows, yes! Probably one of his own relatives!"

"Bueno, que importa? If they are his relatives, then they are yours also. They have always brought me a share of their hunt, all these years. Let them take a beef once in a while!"

"Yes, but they take too many!"

"No, no, my son, it's the bears."

"Oh, you and your bears! . . . I wish the bears would leave us alone and go to the Mission and eat that new friar!"

"Tsch! you mustn't speak that way about a holy friar!"

The young man scowled. "Well, I don't like that holy friar. He looks more like a holy demon to me, with his burning eyes and his long nose. His nose is too long, and besides it is crooked!"

"But what matters the shape of his nose? If he were a horse, I would say yes. But a priest is different."

"No, he is just like a horse, your holy friar. He looks like a horse who had never been well broken. I'll bet that before long he will buck old Fray Bernardo and his corrals to hell!"

"Oh, be silent! Don't bother me with your Mission and your friars! What do I care? . . . Go and saddle your horse! I hope he does buck you off to punish you for your impiety. Someday God will punish you! Go and saddle your horse! . . . I'll clean here!"

"Bueno, bueno, I am going. Don't get angry. But just one thing more. . . . That old Indian who is majordomo at the Mission, you know whom I mean, old Saturnino . . ."

But this time the old man interrupted him with a volley of oaths. He was livid with anger.

"I have already forbidden you time and again to speak to me about him! I don't know who he is, and I don't want to know! If you ever do it again . . ." But the young vaquero was already flying toward the corrals.

Old Esteban Berenda, who flew into such a rage at the mere mention of Saturnino's name, was one of the leather-jacket soldiers who had come with Captain Portola on his first expedition of discovery. He was one of the deserters who preferred taking their chance in the wilderness rather than endure the famous Lieutenant Fages.

And now old Esteban was hardly a white man any longer. When the Indians had found him wandering half-starved and in rags through the canyons, they took pity on him. They fed him. He built a house for himself and that Indian girl he had taken for his wife. He built it of logs and adobe on the little flat overlooking the ocean. There was a spring there. It had been the site of an Indian village, or rancheria, for countless generations.

When the news of the pardon of the deserters had reached him, years before, and he had first dared show himself in the open, he obtained a few cattle and a mare and her foal from the Mission.

He tended them carefully. He begged the Indians not to shoot them, and for a long time the bears were afraid of these new creatures. His herd grew. His little boy grew. He taught him to ride on the old gentle mare. He taught him to throw the reata, a little one at first, on the small calves. It was a hard life and lonely. The boy spoke Spanish with him and Esselen with his mother. His name was Ruiz, but the Indians called him Kinikilali, "Who-is-that?" That was his Indian name. Very soon he was taming colts and lassoing big bulls. He grew up more like an Indian boy than a white man. But after his mother died and he spent most of the time riding with his father, the Spaniard appeared in him, in an odd mixture. And now old Esteban sat for days with his back against the house and Ruiz-Kinikilali rode after the cattle. They roamed everywhere on the hillsides. He did not know how many there were. They roamed on the other side of the ridge into the tangled country and got wild. The Indians shot those when they could. That was all right. The bears or the mountain lions would get them anyhow. The young vaquero rode the ridge constantly, looking for wanderers, trying to drive them back toward the ocean slopes. But it was hard work driving alone. He was secretly teaching Pawi-maliay-hapa "Many Arrows" to ride horseback. Pawi was his cousin and his chum. But Ruis did not tell his father anything about it. It was strictly forbidden to let any gentile Indian ride, and Esteban was an old soldier with a profound respect for orders. Besides he did not want any excuse for the military to come down there and shake him out of his dream. He had been asleep now for ten years, gone back wild, sucked back into the wild country, surrounded by the devils who lived in the air, under the rocks and in the old trees. The Indians arranged matters with these devils and he did not have to bother about them. He felt safe and contented in his solitude, and free to dream away for hours about nothing. He did not want anybody to come and disturb him, priest or soldier.

So, Ruiz did not tell his father that Pawi was learning to ride. Ruiz felt that something must be done. It was all very well for the

old man to say that he didn't care, and what was the use of so
many cattle anyway? At the rate they were going they would have
none left in a few years. The bears were getting more and more
bold and numerous. Esteban would not hunt them any more.
He said it was too dangerous, and besides how could he be sure
that some day they might make a mistake and lasso a bear who
was really a sorcerer in disguise? Maybe there was no such thing
as that, in the midst of the *gente de razon,* in the neighborhood of
towns and churches with the Holy Sacrament to watch over the
country, and he himself was a *cristiano rancio* and believed only in
the God of his ancestors, but he knew also that medicine-men
could change themselves into bears. This was a wild country and
it was true here even though it were not true somewhere else.

   This hunting of bears was a dangerous business. When Esteban settled there, and the bears began to kill his cows, he decided
that he must either get rid of them or lose all his little herd. But of
course he had no rifle, and he had never learned to use a bow and
arrows even to kill small game. His wife's people had always
given him a share of their hunt. But to kill a bear with a bow and
arrow takes a very good hunter, and a very brave one, because a
merely wounded bear is mightily dangerous. So Esteban thought
of a strategem. He could lasso the bear, and this would give time
for his companions to shoot several arrows at short range. It was
an exceedingly risky sort of hunting, because a bear, unlike a
horse or a bull, instead of choking on the reata, will grab it and
pull. If he does not get an arrow through the heart very soon,
there is nothing for it but to let go of the reata and get away as
quickly as possible. Esteban lost many good reatas in this way.
This was serious, because a reata takes the best part of a rawhide
and about three days' work in cutting the long strands and braid-
ing. Not only he lost reatas, but twice he lost his horse: once
when the reata *turns* got too tight around the horn of the saddle
and he had to jump off to save himself, and once when the horse
stumbled and fell, luckily he was thrown headlong and clear of
the animal. Moreover, the hunt had to take place at night, by

moonlight, since it is impossible to get near enough to a bear in the daytime. So Esteban and his helpers would hide in the bushes at night near a cow freshly killed by a bear and wait for him to come back to the carcass for another meal. Esteban had a good horse, a "caballo de reata," that is, a horse at once quick and obedient, a horse that could jump ten feet from a standstill on the merest tap of a spur and yet not dance a fandango after ten minutes of hard work cutting herd, "arrebatar," as they call it. Ruiz had a horse not quite so good, too nervous. As soon as he heard the bear coming crackling through the brush and smelled the pungent, disquieting smell, he would begin to snort. And Ruiz himself, in the first years when he began to hunt with his father, sitting there on his horse in the dark, with the reata unslung and the loop all ready, waiting there in the shadow, peering into the moonlit space and trying to rehearse all the turns and twists, when he heard the crackling and snapping in the chaparral, coming, and stopping, and coming again, and stopping, and coming again, his spurs went ting-a-ling-ling, he just couldn't help it though he heard his father cursing him in his beard and the Indians sniggering.

Ruiz was left-handed with the reata, and that helped a great deal because between both of them they could stretch the bear nicely. Then the Indians would fill him with arrows, almost point blank. The whole thing was done quickly, silently, in the space of an Ave Maria after Esteban shouted "Ahora!" and the two horses dashed out into the moonlight. Then the Indians would stamp a short dance of expiation around the dead bear, going three times around one way, then back the other way round once, and calling him "Elder Brother, Chief, now are you happy!"

The old man would coil his reata and go home. Ruiz-Kinikilali used to lag behind, coiling and recoiling his reata, watching the dance, feeling queer and upset. And one night he just naturally took his place in the row of stamping men, but he never told his father this.

And now Esteban Berenda was getting old and did not hunt

bears any more. He sat in the sun in front of his house and watched the sea. Maybe the Philippine galleon would appear soon on its way south. He sat in the sun and blinked at the sea. He was thinking of his dead wife, the Indian woman. She had been fat and silent. He sat in the sun, blinking, looking at a pueblo of whitewashed houses shimmering in the haze. He didn't hunt any more. He didn't even ride after the cattle any more. Let Ruiz attend to that. He was young. Let the bears kill a few cows. It did not matter. Plenty of cattle yet, grazing on the sunny hillsides. Let the Indians shoot a few on the other side of the ridge. It did not matter. They were his own people, or his wife's, or his son's anyway. Ruiz, they called him Kinikilali. Which was the better name? He sat in front of his house, blinking in the sun, on the little flat, and the ocean stretching away blue and sparkling.

His wife had been dead now for more than ten years. He had wanted to bury her, but her relatives insisted on burning her body. He usually let them have their way. It was so far to the Mission, a full day's ride on a good horse. He hardly ever went there, and as for the Presidio, he shunned it altogether. If they wanted to burn her body, let them do it. After all, she belonged to them. He himself would always remain a good Cristiano, but the Mission was so far, and he had lived all alone here for so long, he did not know what to think any more, and perhaps their ways were the best ways for this kind of country. After all, it was their country and they knew her, they knew her spirits, all kinds of people who lived in the air or inside the trees, some of them were birds or animals. The padres called them devils. Perhaps they were devils. Esteban did not know. He was not versed in theology. He himself had never seen a devil, and the Indians had always been good to him. He liked them but, for all the years he had lived among them he had never gotten to know them. He had never even gotten to know his wife. He had loved her very deeply, and after she died he always felt lonely.

Esteban was old and he sat on a stump with his back to the house, looking at the ocean. He sat for hours looking at the ocean. He sat looking at the ocean, dreaming.

Sometimes a ship hove in sight, way out at sea, a galleon from the Philippines, homeward bound with her cargo. Such ships headed straight for Cape Mendocino and then sailed south along the coast, bound for the ports of Lower California and the coast of Sinaloa. Their sight excited him strangely.

The old man sat on his stump, looking at the ocean, dreaming. He would never go home now. He thought of the sun-baked plains of La Mancha and a pueblo of white houses shimmering in the haze.

Why didn't he saddle his horse and look at the cattle? Oh! What did he care about cattle now! Let his boy do the riding. He was young.

It is a strange country, that wild Coast of the Esselen Indians, where Esteban had taken refuge, a strange country, beckoning from afar. Curiously enough it is almost impossible to get there. And yet it is not a case of burning deserts or impassable snows. The country lies smiling under a pleasant sky, with water in every brook and long grass on the hillsides. True enough, it is everywhere exceedingly steep, and the canyons wind in very tortuous fashion, so that the whole country is a labyrinth without any natural avenues. This may account partly for the unsettled state of the region even at the present day. But there must be something else. There must be some reason why every time you try to get into that country you find yourself balked and finally turning back after much fatigue. Why does that place keep itself so remote, as if holding a secret, brooding under the sun? It lies at the edge of the water, rising like a wall, gazing moodily over the same ocean, towards China and the other side of the world. And back of the wall there are the deep canyons, and the tall pines, and the hillsides of brush in the mysterious glare of noontime. What does it mean? How can a thing be so wild that is so full of life and charming variety, of young trees and deer grazing in the gay clearings, of the chatter of bluejays, and the red trunks of the madronyos. And yet it is so wild in there that you cry with the loneliness of it. You feel a creeping panic in your heart. Perhaps it is because we are civilized and do not understand these things. We have other gods, and we can no longer pray to the tree.

At any rate this is the place where Fray Luis wished to proselyte. He knew that the Esselen lived in there. They were "gentiles," unconverted Indians. They never came to the Missions. They were utterly pagan. Fray Luis burned with desire to convert them. He kept thinking about it.

He had found it impossible to reach the Esselen from San Antonio, but he thought he might perhaps succeed from Carmel. And that is why when he came to that Mission he decided to go directly by the coast line. Nobody else but Fray Luis would have been foolhardy enough to try it. But he succeeded and managed to come through, as we have seen in his diary. On that trip he saw no Indian rancherias. Several times he saw small parties of Indians at a distance, but although he called to them and made friendly signs they always vanished from sight. And yet he had the feeling that he was constantly watched. A queer sensation to go through those wild lonely woods and feel all the time that someone is watching you. You can imagine the deer scattering at the approach of his mule. In his diary he calls it a donkey but it was probably a mule. The son of Don Aniceto would have called a mule a donkey. And in the distance, parties of brown men, stark naked as were the Indians of those days, with the bow in the left hand, the arrows under the right arm-pit. They would not stop when he called them.

How is it that Fray Luis had missed the little flat with the house of Esteban on that memorable journey from San Antonio Mission, when he had pushed and dragged his mule for three days through the wilderness? He could have seen it easily from the place where the trail from the beach crosses the ridge, a trail made by generations of Indians. It climbs like a staircase from the rocky shore more than three thousand feet below, up, up, steeper and steeper, over the face of the limestone cliff, hot like a furnace. It emerges on the summit of the ridge and then plunges down on the other side, down into the canyada where another Indian village stood on a sheltered flat. Here there were more of the conical huts, and also a ceremonial house with its smoke-hole door on the roof. This other village, deep in the canyon, was hidden from the ridge, but the little flat on the ocean slope could easily be seen. Yet Fray Luis missed it.

Perhaps he was looking the other way, or perhaps it was in the late afternoon when he passed, that strange time when the spirit of anguish is abroad, leading fear by the hand, and he was looking for a good camping place, hurrying, oppressed. That time in the late afternoon, when the sun is low over the water and the deer come out of the canyadas to graze on the little flats and on the hillsides. Go there some day and sit down with your back against a tree. Keep quiet, do not move, keep very quiet. Just sit there, still as a stone.

Do you hear what the jays are saying over your head, up there in the branches? Bluejay is saying: "Hey! who is that there? Are you asleep or dead? Dead man, I guess, went to sleep there and died. That's all right, Mr. Squirrel, walk right over him, don't be afraid, come right up. Some nice pine cones on this tree, up there at the top. Just getting ripe and the nuts still juicy and fresh. Only don't drop the scales right over me! My gracious, haven't you got any manners? . . . Come right up, Mr. Deer, come right up this way, and nobody in sight, fine grass for Mrs. Deer and the little Fawn, fat little fawn, how old is he? Say . . . just look at that Woodpecker, will you? Did you ever see anybody so busy? Peck, peck, peck, woodpecker, now go get another nut. Fine for Mrs. Bluejay, Chief Bluejay, that's my name. Hard winter, plenty nuts and acorns in little holes, thank you, Mr. Chief Woodpecker, because I am sure you are a chief also. . . . Sh! look out there everybody! I hear someone coming along the trail. . . . I hear a horse's footfalls. . . . I hear the jingling of spurs. . . . Quick, Deer, run, run!"

A vaquero passes along the trail, slouching in the saddle.

BLUEJAY: "That's right! You own the world, don't you. . . . Well, you can come back now, Mr. Deer. He's gone. Why! look who is here, Chief Weasel himself and Mr. Coyote."

COYOTE: "You mean Mr. Chief Coyote, don't you? Chief Coyote, Doctor Coyote, that's me. Everybody knows me. I am the one. I am a chief, I am a medicine-man. I am a runner, I can run fast, I know all kinds of running songs, I made the world, at least I made half of it, the worst half, that's the best half . . ."

BLUEJAY: "Well, then, why didn't you make a woman for yourself, even half of one? Where is your wife, eh?"

COYOTE: "Hey! Hey! I have no wife. I have no wife. I must go look for a wife. I can't stop here talking with you. I must go look for a wife."

WEASEL: "I see some people coming up the trail from below."

BLUEJAY: "Yes, I have been watching them, too. Just Indians . . . with a load of abalones and mussels. How slow they are going. Must be a heavy load. That's all right, Mr. Deer, plenty of time, plenty of time."

Three men and a woman appear on the ridge. The men are entirely naked. The woman wears a grass skirt. They all carry pack-baskets on their backs, slung from the forehead. The woman's is smaller and slung from a strap across the chest, just above the breasts. They bulge from under it. They are all panting heavily. They squat on their hams, to ease their packs on the ground. They say nothing.

BLUEJAY: "That's right, take a rest, boys . . . and girl. Nice girl, that, just right for Coyote, but maybe not big enough! Ha! Ha! Long climb up here, boys, and quite a way to the rancheria, yet. And how was the fishing? Well, you might answer something, you dummies! Aw, they don't know anything. Not a one of them is a medicine-man. Just common Indians. That's right, get up and on your way, you have got quite a bit of trail, yet, even if it is downhill, and the sun is getting pretty low. . . ."

WEASEL: "Who were they? I don't know any of them."

BLUEJAY: "Oh, some fellows from the rancheria down there. I have seen them before. Just common people, nobody in particular. Ho-hum . . . I am getting sleepy. Sun is almost in the water. I feel all tired out . . . working too hard. . . . I don't know what you people would do without me. Well, good-night, Father Sun, I think your brother is coming out pretty soon. Here, move away, you, that's my twig. . . ."

WEASEL: "I have a brother in that rancheria. A fine young Indian. Pawi-maliay-hapa, that's his name. Fine young fellow. Good hunter. He always calls me when he is going on a hunt. He has got my song and I lead him to the game. I go ahead and I wait for him. I sit on a rock and wait for him to catch up. I lead him to the game. I like that young fellow. He knows my song. He always remembers to call me."

A CRICKET: "I know somebody in that rancheria too. He is my father. An old blind man. He is a doctor. He is a powerful doctor. He knows lots of songs. He knows songs for everything."

A puma comes along the trail, in the moonlight.

PUMA: "I know the one you mean. He is my father, too, that old blind man. He knows my song. I heard him calling a while ago, down there, but I am not going right now. I am hungry. I am going to hunt tonight. A nice fat deer for me."

He stretches himself lazily. He looks at the moon rising over the Ventanas and lets out a long, querying roar. It makes a beetle jump.

THE BEETLE: "Great Scott, man! Couldn't you give us a warning? Look how you woke that little owl."

THE OWL: "No, I wasn't asleep. I was just thinking . . . I was thinking about these new people, these white people . . . I wonder who they are. . . ."

THE BEETLE: "Well, Sir, I'll tell you what I know, which is what I heard a grandfather of mine tell me when I was a little boy. He used to tell about some people on the other side of the water. Very powerful people, he said, and very wise. They knew a great many things, more than these Indians. That's what I heard my grandfather tell. And I have figured it out from the way he said they lived, that these new white men are the same people . . . except that they are foolish, that's what I don't understand, unless it is that they have forgotten what they used to know. Or maybe their heart got all dried up inside of them. . . ."

A PINE TREE: "You are an old man, Beetle, and you talk too much. I am older than you and yet . . ."

A REDWOOD: "Whenever the wind blows the pine trees have to talk."

THE VENTANA GONE TO THE SANTA LUCIA PEAK: "You look all gray, old man, in the moonlight."

SANTA LUCIA PEAK: "Shut up!"

An Indian's voice rises in the night, a young voice, singing: "Hey-hey-hey-ho-he-hey . . . my heart is crying . . . where is my power? . . . hey-hey-hey-ho . . . you have taken my power away . . . tumas! iyo! come, my spirits, come, my power . . . she left me because I am ugly and crooked . . . she left me . . . hey-hey-hey . . . my heart is crying. . . ."

THE NIGHT WIND: "I am cold and dry. I am lonely."

3
The Devil sets a Trap

Meanwhile, at the Mission of the Carmel, Fray Luis was catechizing his especial neophyte, that girl who had run away from the Esselen tribe. He had other neophytes also to instruct, men and women from the Rumsen tribe, mostly people from the Carmel Valley and from the rancherias along the lower part of the Salinas River, but he was especially interested in the Esselen girl because she was the only Esselen at the Mission. It was the first time that anyone from that wild tribe had been persuaded to leave the mountains and come to the Mission. In fact she had come of her own free will. She had appeared there, one morning, foot-sore and hungry, and very shy, just a few days before Fray Luis ar-

rived. She was of course a godsend for that friar whose very am-
bition was precisely to bring the light of the true God to the wild
Esselens. And so he spent more of his time learning the Esselen
language from her than teaching her the catechism.

He wrote in that curious diary of his:

"Dia de Sta. Gertrudis, Virgin, and a most beautiful day, too, with an
amethyst tint spread over the valley. I called this to the attention of Fray
Bernardo. 'Yes, yes,' quoth he, 'very beautiful, very beautiful, and just
think, my dear Fray Luis, just think of how much grain could be raised
here and exported if only the home Government were not so short-

sighted in its policy!' . . . and he went on to explain a lot of things which I did not understand. That Catalan has a head on his shoulders! I also asked my little wild beauty what they call that color in her language. She said there was no name for it, but it made her think of the inside of an abalone shell. I asked why. 'Because it isn't real,' she answered. She says things like that, all the time, that make me restless. And then when I try to teach her the catechism I find her stupid. Strange little animal! But anyway she is a good teacher when it comes to language. Only, what a devil of a language! You say everything upside down. It reminds me more of the Sextapay of San Antonio than of the Rumsen of these parts. As soon as I know enough of it I am going down into that country. I am burning to convert these poor wild Esselenes. Something is drawing me to that place. I have been dreaming of it, several times, curious dreams, almost nightmares. I must go there. I did not come here to get fat and lazy. As soon as I know enough of the language I will go. God will help me . . . and if He has reserved me for the fate of the martyrs, blessed be His will, say I. What more do I crave than to expiate my sins? What could be sweeter than to forget? . . . I must make a friend of that young vaquero. He may be able to help me. They say that his father and he are the only white men living down there, and that they are on good terms with the Indians. The young fellow was here again last night. I must say I don't like him, and I don't know why. There is something subtly insolent in his bearing. It's not his manners. He is boorish enough, but so is everybody in this country. For the matter of that, he is not half as boorish as the people of the Presidio, the Commander of the garrison included, and they have not the excuse of having been raised like an animal of the wilds. . . . Fray Luis! remember that you are no longer in Salamanca, this cassock is not a cappa, remember above all that this crucifix is not the hilt of your sword. Ah! my sword, my lovely, my pretty, where are you? Is it a sin to remember you, and your lithe body, my mistress, my very myself? Is it a sin? Is it not enough to stand with patience and humility this fellow's searching gaze? And how well he rides! I believe that is what I am jealous of. What a figure he would make in the streets of Sevilla! . . . Bah! This is an edifying diary I keep. Shame on you, Fray Luis, pray, Fray Luis, you unworthy monk, take your breviary and pray, I'll discipline you, I'll make you forget, I'll scourge you, the lash for you, the lash for the devil in you. . . . . . .

I don't know how many strokes I gave my poor back, enough anyway to bring the blood . . . but I feel better, I will sleep peacefully tonight. Saint Gertrudis, you noble virgin, I offer my pain to you. I offer it for this poor Indian girl, take her under your protection. . . . Nine o'clock! To bed, to bed, three hours only before Matins and the shaking hand of Fray Tallow on my shoulder. How I do hate to hear his Catalan rasp from under my dreams, 'Come, come, Fray Luis, up with you, it's almost a quarter past midnight. Come, come, to the chapel, don't be so lazy' . . . well, to bed!"

Look at these two men at Matins, in the echoing empty church, just these two, on either side of the nave, each one with a candle to his book, throwing back and forth the versicle and the response, the two voices alternating in sonorous cadence, monotonously for an hour, while outside the constellations swing around the pole toward the chilly dawn. Ah! the wonderful technique in all ritual, this losing of one's own self into the magma of a cosmic rhythm, the dissolving of the individual and his pain, and his sorrow, and all that effort to hold the self together. To stamp a chant around a drum under the moon, or to swing a psalm in the gloom of the nave, two techniques for two cultures, but the same psychological problem, at bottom, and after all very much the same treatment. . . . Therein lies the beauty of prayer in common. And therefore it was a wise monastic rule that held these two friars to what may seem an almost meaningless, an unnecessary formality. Two monks holding Matins by themselves, just exactly as if they had been a whole congregation. It makes one think of those white men who live alone in the tropics, and dress every evening for supper. Two monks, two white monks, isolated in their Mission, on the outskirts of a not even very civilized colony, and surrounded by more than a hundred so-called "converts," and several thousand not far outside the Mission adobe walls, in all the rancherias, practicing actively all the rites of magic and sorcery, these two white monks they had need, indeed, to hold on tight to all the forms and formalities of their own culture . . . one of these two especially.

At the Carmel Mission old Saturnino was the *mayordomo*. That is to say, he was a combination of sacristan and Indian chief. The tribe under his care were the Indians corralled inside the Mission adobe walls. He bullied them, especially the neophytes. Very few people remembered his Indian name. He was Saturnino, *el mayordomo,* and one of the oldest and first converts. He said he was a Rumsen, from one of the furthest villages up the valley. But the older Indians at the Mission smiled ironically at this. According to them that village up the valley had only been his hiding place for a while, a certain long time ago, when he had run away from the vengeance of his own Esselen tribe. He had relatives at that rancheria up the valley, and they hid him for a while. But he would not tell them what it was he had done. After a time they advised him to take refuge at the Mission which had then just been started. But all that was long ago, nobody remembered very much about it, and if old Saturnino caught you talking about it, or even suspected you were talking about it, down came your portion of pozole at the next meal. And it would be no use complaining to the padre, because the mayordomo would simply say that he had heard you swearing, and the padre would believe him.

Saturnino had charge of the pozoleria, of the chapel, and of the "nunnery." It was he who saw to it that all the unmarried women were in there at nightfall before he locked the door, and then he turned the key over to Fray Bernardo. He enjoyed locking them up for the night. He also had charge of the routine catechization of the neophytes. He lined them up in the morning. They squatted on the ground. He squatted on a chair in front of them, with his feet on the edge of the seat. When a padre appeared in the offing he put his feet down. When the padre had disappeared the feet went up again. He sing-songed: "Our Father," and the Indians in front of him repeated, "our father." They knew that tolerably well. He sing-songed: "who art in heaven," they repeated something very close to it. He sing-songed: "may thy reign come." They mumbled something. He sing-songed: "may thy will." There was a feeble murmur. He sing-songed: "be done on earth as well as in heaven." Only one or two voices answered in a jumble of Rumsen words that sounded faintly like the Spanish. Saturnino would roll his eyes and click his tongue, and look significantly toward the pozoleria, & then he would fairly shout: "Give us our daily bread." Everybody woke up and repeated: "Give us our daily bread." And so on, by lulls and storms for an hour. After which they went back to work with a sigh of relief.

And he went back to his reatas. They were his joy, his love, his consolation. He was a reata-maker. He kept his materials in the pozoleria, thongs of rawhide, long, very long strips, of an even width all the way for the forty or fifty feet of their length, cut as they had been from a single hide, round and round the edge. His tools, an old razor blade, a whetstone, a deer's antler for a marlinspike, and his teeth. He made reatas for the vaqueros of Monterey, and sold them. That was all his little benefice.

When a vaquero came to the Mission old Saturnino would ask: "And how is the reata?" as one might say: how is your baby? And sometimes they would bring him a reata for repair. If it was one of his own make, he would almost weep. He would cry: "But how did it happen? Don't tell me! You have been dragging firewood with it, or you staked your horse. Don't tell me no, don't tell me you broke it in the corral. My reatas don't break in the corral. My reatas will hold the biggest bull. Don't my reatas hold bears? Look at old Esteban, down the Coast to the south, he always tries to keep one of my reatas saved away for hunting bears. But that shameless son of his always steals them, and then he does just like you, he drags logs with it down the mountain. Don't tell me no. I know you did. Well, I will repair it this time, but this is the last time. All right, go and sin no more." This last remark said not at all as a joke but very seriously. He and Fray Bernardo had had several arguments about it. Saturnino could see no impiety in it. Fray Bernardo was totally lacking in the sense of humor.

The afternoon was dragging lazily over the Mission.

The Mission was like a little town surrounded by a wall. Besides the church, there were the Indian quarters for the unmarried men, the Indian quarters for the girls (also called the nunnery), the pozoleria or kitchen where the mush was cooked in a great cauldron, the carpenter shop, various storerooms. One corner of the great courtyard was occupied by a crew of Indians making adobe bricks, and was known as the adoberia. Some were mixing the clay with the straw. Others were pouring the mixture in the molds. Rows of adobes in all stages of drying were arrayed on the ground. Even when everything else was silent in the Mission there was activity in the adoberia, and somebody was singing there. Sometimes a single voice, repeating over and over the same monotonous air. Sometimes a chorus, with a thud of stamping feet to mark the cadence. The padres knew that many of the songs were of a religious character, but they did not know which. On the other hand many of the songs were love songs, gambling songs, hunting songs, and the like.

It was wise to let the prisoners have some consolation. Most padres were men like Fray Bernardo, little given to speculation, content with sincere outward conformity. They got along fairly well with the Indians. They made them work, and were pretty severe in meting out punishment, at times. But they were not curious. They left the Indians alone as to their inner life. They did not ask questions. They were blissfully ignorant alike of all beliefs and customs of the unconverted or gentile living all over the country, and of all the gossip that went on inside the walls of the Mission. The adoberia was of course the clearing-house or exchange for all the news. If a sorcerer caused the death of someone in a distant village, the fact was soon discussed and commented on in the adoberia. There were all kinds of intrigues and jealousies carried on. Some of the Indians were suspected by the others of "squealing" to the padres. Some of the Indians had really become sincerely habituated to their conversion. But most of them had been forcibly brought in by the dragoons, and baptized without their knowing it. Unbaptized neophytes were supposed to be still free to leave the Mission at their will, but converts belonged to the Mission and could not leave it.

Men like Fray Luis were rare. The Indians hated them. Fray Luis would never have made anybody work. He himself did not care whether he ate pozole or a juicy piece of venison. Material wealth was a very difficult thing for him to keep his mind on. Nor had he any sense of discipline. If he saw an Indian climbing over the wall he would never think of shouting an alarm, for the simple reason that the fact made no impression on his mind. But he was forever asking questions, forever thrusting his long nose into their private affairs. At any moment you might suddenly realize that he had been standing silently over you in plain sight, listening to your conversation, while you and a friend were heatedly discussing some tribal affair. And already he understood a lot of Rumsen. As for Esselen, that fool of a girl was teaching him. He wanted to know all about the Indian religion, as if that were any business for the white man. The few who were his especially reserved catechumens feared him even more. They longed for the days of Saturnino's classes. They dreaded this long thin torturer with the burning eyes and the long febrile hands shooting out of the brown sleeves. He was not content with "yes" and "no," he was not content with even a faultless repetition of prayers, he forced you to think and to know why this was so and so. He asked questions, he made you think, he made your head ache. He took possession of you and made you his slave. He was not even good-naturedly paternal like Fray Bernardo, with a kind of smile of approval and a pat on the head. His eyes burned and grew wide. He talked and talked. He made you feel like him. He made you see all sorts of things. Then he would leave you abruptly and walk off to his cell without a word, his long legs striding across the courtyard, and you felt chilly all of a sudden and looked up to see if there was a cloud. But no, the sun was beating down as usual. The crew was working in the adoberia. You knew they had been watching you, suspecting you. They would ask: "What does the old coyote want to know, now? What did you tell him? He is a sorcerer himself, watch out for him, don't tell him anything, he knows too much already!"

That was one of the peculiarities of Fray Luis. He would go straight across the courtyard, instead of following the arcades all around like any dignified person. Fray Bernardo once tried to remonstrate with him. Fray Bernardo was Father Superior after all. He first put the matter to him plainly, but Fray Luis did not seem to understand what he meant. So Fray Bernardo explained patiently that it was necessary to be dignified on account of the Indians. Fray Bernardo was rubbing his fat hands nervously. Fray Luis stood stooping over him, looking at him intently. Fray Bernardo began to perspire, and his face got red. He lost his presence of mind completely. He mumbled: "Well, never mind, do as you like, it doesn't matter anyway," and proceeded right across the courtyard to his own cell. He was trotting as usual when he was agitated. Fray Luis went around the arcades with his own legs. . . . They arrived at the same moment at the doors of their cells, which were contiguous. Fray Luis waited for Fray Bernardo to pass and open his door. Then he passed by, and opened his own door. Fray Bernardo slammed his door shut. A few minutes later he could hear Fray Luis scourging himself. Fray Bernardo sighed: "What a saint! But he will drive me crazy!"

The afternoon was dragging lazily over the Mission.

There was a lull in the adoberia. The boom of the breakers on the beach drifted over the walls. Gulls flew overhead on their way to the laguna. Old Saturnino was plaiting a reata in his corner. Sunlight filled the courtyard.

Fray Luis was instructing his Esselen girl. He sat on the ground of the arcade with his back against a column, his knees drawn up under his chin, his long hands grasping his ankles. The sun had moved and was beating down on him, but he did not seem to notice it. The girl kept retreating and retreating with the shade. She was getting sleepier and sleepier. But she opened her eyes more and more wide in listening. She liked his voice. She wished he would never stop. Once she went to sleep completely, and had a short dream. She woke up with a start. She winked several times. Then she laid her head against his knees. Then she began very, very gently to snore. When he heard the snore, Fray Luis stopped instantly, and his face went white. The interruption made the girl stop her breathing. She moved uneasily and her head almost rolled off Fray Luis' knees. His long hand shot out and pushed the head back on his knees. The girl's bosom resumed its regular heaving. Fray Luis was still pale with anger. He murmured: "Imbecile!" Then with great careful movements he reached for his rosary and commenced telling his beads. The sun now was reaching her body sprawled there, her face buried in the monk's robe. She was snoring quite loudly. Fray Bernardo trotted by. He stopped with a jerk. His jaw dropped. Then a wide smile spread over his face. He put his finger to his lips and with a large wink he tiptoed by. Fray Luis had not even seen him. He was telling his beads, looking at the seagulls circling overhead with shrill cries. Several Indians passed by, with wide grins on their faces. The adoberia was buzzing with suppressed laughter.

BANG! BANG! BANG! E-e-e-e-i-ya-Hou!! Abren las puertas! No esten dormidos! Dispiertense, que aqui viene la costa del Sur! Wake up! Wake up and open the doors, for here comes a rider from the south!

Everybody jumped up. The door-man scrambled to his feet. The adoberos stopped drinking and gossiping, with broad smiles on their faces. The girl stopped snoring and woke up. Fray Luis snapped his rosary in anger. The knocking on the massive gates of the patio continued, and now a rollicking song in Spanish came from the other side, in a high tenor voice. Every verse was of four lines and the last line was in the Esselen language. All the Indians were roaring with laughter.

The great gates were opened. A vaquero dashed through, with his horse, in a whirlwind of dust. He pulled up half-way to the center, and all those in the adoberia could see him stick his spur in the under part of the belly back of the cincha. The horse started on a crazy round of bucking, twisting, sunfishing, back-hopping, and every other sort of misbehaviour. The Indians were roaring and yelling. Fray Bernardo came out of his cell, hurriedly buttoning his cassock, and winking in the strong sunlight.

When he saw him, Kinikilali stroked his horse's neck and made him quit. He jumped off and kissed Fray Bernardo's hand. Fray Bernardo made the sign of the Cross on the boy's forehead, then raised him and embraced him.

"And where do you come from, now?"

"Well, Your Reverence sent for me and here I am. I started last night just before sundown, and I took a good sleep at the Little River, and then I came up, and here I am at your orders. . . ."

"Bueno, bueno, chico, muy bien. . . . All the cattle are spread all over the place, everywhere, and we are losing them. All these boys from Monterey are no good. They are all right with the guitar, and some of them can throw the reata, but I can't depend on them. And anyway I can't have them around here with so many girls in the nunnery. I need you. You must bring in all the cattle that belong to the Mission. We will brand the calves."

"But, Father, how can I bring them in with me alone on a horse. You know I can't do it!"

"Sh! sh! sh! Some of them can ride . . . but everybody afoot as soon as you get down into the valley, you hear me?"

"All right, little grandfather. I'll send for my cousin. He is a good rider already . . . sh! sh!"

They both laughed.

"Father, I have to go to Monterey, tonight . . ."

"Go with God, my son."

Ruiz Berenda, or Kinikilali, kissed Fray Bernardo's hand. Then he turned and leaped in the saddle. He gave another yell, the doors opened, and he went out bucking in a swirl of dust. The massive gates creaked shut again.

The girl had slunk away long ago. Fray Luis was still sitting with his back against the pillar, telling his beads. The rays of the sun struck his face slantingly, with sudden patches of dark shadow on one side.

The late afternoon was descending on the Mission. The seagulls were returning overhead. It grew chilly. Fray Luis got up and strode across the courtyard to the Church.

4
And baits it

Ruiz was riding along the Ridge, his gaze wandering over the chaparral, peering down into the woods, looking for straying cattle. He was riding along, lazily, sitting sideways in the saddle, but silent. He very seldom sang. He was riding along the Ridge on a hot afternoon. The saddle leathers creaked, the spurs made a jingling tinkle in cadence. The horse walked with a long-gaited stride.

The vaquero heard a whistle behind him, and stopped. He turned and saw Pawi hurrying after him along the trail. Pawi was his cousin on his mother's side. That is, Pawi's mother and his own mother had been sisters. So they called each other "elder brother," and "younger brother," in the Indian language. But they were nearly of the same age. Pawi was a good hunter. When he went out hunting, he observed all the rules. He abstained from any meat. He rubbed himself with bear grease. He called to the Four Masters of the Hunt, Puma, Bear, Eagle, Fish-Hawk. Then he called to whatever it was he was going to hunt: "Brother, you must let me kill you. My people are hungry. We need food. You must not run away and hide." Then he called to his own medicine, who was Weasel: "Come, my power, tumas iyo! Come Weasel, come my power, lead me to the game, lead me to the deer." Pawi-maliay-hapa was a good hunter.

Pawi was ordinarily a gay sort of fellow, rather reckless, ready for any kind of fun. He had high cheekbones and eyes that gave one a curious impression of being able to stretch lengthwise. His hair was very long, reaching almost to his waist. He usually wore it tightly wound in a knot. Then when he let it loose, it waved over his back like a stallion's mane.

But he looked worried that day, and full of concern, as he hurried after Ruiz. The vaquero had dismounted and sat on a log, holding his horse by a long horsehair rope. Pawi greeted him: "Hey! brother."

"Hey! brother," answered Ruiz, and he added, "Where were you?"

"Down there at the spring by the fallen madronyo. I saw you pass along the ridge and I hurried after you. Listen! brother, there is a dead cow down there, by the spring. Something is wrong."

The vaquero sat still and said nothing for a long time. He was looking at the ocean. Pawi was squatting, idly toying with an arrow. He would curve it between his fingers, and then sight down the shaft to see if it was straight. Finally Ruiz-Kinikilali broke the silence, "It was a bear that killed her, wasn't it?" he asked.

"Yes."

Another long silence. Then the vaquero spoke: "That makes three since the month began!" There was bitterness and anger in his voice. He added, "I wish my father would wake up! Some day a bear will eat him, too, right where he sits dreaming all day. At this rate, there will be no cattle left before the rains. And just when we were getting a good herd! It seems a shame. Listen, Pawi, Pawi-maliay-hapa, we must do something!" Pawi did not answer, he kept on straightening arrows between his fingers. Ruiz spoke again. "I tell you we must kill that bear, you and I, just we two. Let the old man dream away on his stump. We don't need him. We can kill that bear ourselves, you and I. This horse is good, now, under the reata. And you never had a better bow than this one."

Pawi smiled. "Yes, it is a good, strong bow. That was very springy sinew I backed it with. It was from the neck of that young horse who broke his leg, you remember? Do you know, Kiniki-lali, I think that horse sinew is better than deer. Let's kill all the horses, Kini, and make sinew. Then we will go to the white village and kill all the soldiers and the medicine-men with the long skirts and make sinew of them too. Maybe they would make even better sinew than horses."

He was laughing. Now he stood up to test his bow, and show his chum how far he could shoot with the bow backed with horse sinew. With one end stuck in the ground, he bent the other end across his knee and strung it. Now he picked out an arrow, and straightened it. Now he knocked it, and he began the draw. He was standing with his feet close together, body slightly bent forward from the straight muscular thighs and a little to the left, as if about to fall, just poised over. He let fly, and kept his position for a second, the right hand drawn back almost to the cheek, his eyes following the flight of the arrow. It descended and stuck in the ground far away. Pawi turned back to his cousin with a smile of pride. Then he squatted again, and once more looked worried. He looked at the ground for awhile, then looked at Ruiz full in the face, and said slowly, "I don't like it, little brother."

"Why not? You are not afraid, Pawi, I know you are not afraid."

"Yes, I am afraid, of course, I am afraid. You don't know who that bear is."

"Neither do you."

"No, I don't. But he may be somebody just the same. I don't like it, I tell you. Even suppose he is just a bear and not a person, it's too risky hunting him without your father's help. How are you going to keep him from grabbing the reata, if there is only one reata on him?"

"Oh don't worry about that. Anyway that's what you will be there for, to shoot him full of arrows before he gets to my end of the reata. And if he does get too close, well, I'll let go of the turns and all I lose is a good reata and a bear-skin. Listen, brother, just think of all the bear grease you will get, all for yourself, nobody to divide with. Maybe you will get four hands of bead-strings in exchange at the Rumsen villages. It seems the bears are leaving their country. . . . I wonder if that is why there are so many around here."

The two of them were silent for awhile. The afternoon was stretching towards evening. Pawi spoke again: "I will help you . . . but I don't like it, I tell you. I will help you, because I can't say no to you. You keep after me like that and I can't help myself, although I know it is no good. This morning I started out to hunt and I looked for my protector that Weasel. Pretty soon I saw him ahead of me on the trail. He was leading me to the game, as usual, running on ahead and stopping on a rock or on top of a log, waiting for me to catch up. Then I got thirsty and I went to the spring of the Fallen Madronyo to get a drink. That is where I saw the dead cow. I was looking at the tracks of that bear and Weasel got angry. He did not want me to stop there, he did not want me to stay there. He kept jumping up and down, and scolding. He would run off and come back to scold and run off again. That's when I saw you. I wish now I had listened to him."

Ruiz laughed, "Leave your Weasel alone. What does Weasel know about hunting bears? He may be all right for game without hearts, like deer and rabbits, but he doesn't know anything about bears. Your Weasel is a coward. . . ."

"Hush, Kinikilali, you fool! He might hear you." And Pawi peered all around suspiciously. He was scared and angry. "What do you speak like that for? Are you trying to spoil my luck? What's the matter with you?" He was glaring at his cousin. Ruiz tried to pass it off as a joke. But Pawi was angry now.

"Kini, I wish you were all Indian, like us."

"I am Indian enough, big brother. I don't like the whites."

"Then why do you do the things you do?"

"What is it that I do? What are you scolding me for, now?"

"You know very well. I mean that woman."

"There you are! I knew you were going to come out with that, sooner or later. Well, what about it? Can I help it if the woman left her husband? I had nothing to do with it."

"Some people say that you did not, and again some people say that you did."

"No, I did not, Pawi. She left him because she was afraid of his medicine. She says that he had too much power and she was afraid of it. She says it was his power that killed their little child. It was too strong and it killed the child. She says he was not careful enough. He came into her camp right after curing sick people, and sometimes he still had his medicine hat with him, even with a new devil he had just caught, stuck right there in among the feathers. I don't blame her for leaving him."

"Yes, he is too careless, I know that. Young doctors are careless. But why do you have to get mixed up with it? Why did you take her down there, down to the white man's camp?"

"I did not take her down there, Pawi. She went there herself."

"But you go there all the time too. Our people have heard about it from the Rumsen. They say that you are making love to her."

"And what if I do! I have a right to. She has no husband."

"Yes she has a husband. Her people never paid back the marriage gifts. Hualala is still her husband, till the gifts are paid back."

"Well, his people have not paid back what she gave for him, either."

"They don't have to. It was she who left him."

"Yes, but it was his fault."

"Who says that? I have not heard the chiefs say that, and they are the ones to decide."

"What do the chiefs say, Pawi?" Ruiz was eager now.

"I don't know. They are not talking yet, but the people are grumbling. Some people are very angry with you. Some people say Hualala has a right to kill you now."

"I am not afraid of him!"

"You had better be! He is a powerful doctor, even if he is young. His medicine is strong and it will surely kill you if he sends it after you. His medicine will do it, I know, because he has a right to kill you, as far as I can see."

Ruiz-Kinikilali was beginning to be a little frightened for all his customary insouciance. He said plaintively, "Are you also against me, brother?"

"No, I am not against you, but what can I do? I can't protect you against his medicine. You ought to have some strong power to work against his. You ought to get some strong doctor to work for you. You are rich, you can hire a good doctor."

"What about the old blind man, Amomuths?"

Pawi laughed bitterly. "That's all you can think of!"

"Isn't he the most powerful doctor around here?"

"Sure he is! But he is the girl's grandfather, too!"

"No, he isn't! I know very well who he is. He is my mother's uncle."

"Let me see. . . . Yes, that's right, he is. Well, that only makes it worse for you and that girl, because you and she must be some kind of distant blood relations. I don't know what the old people will say about it. They are sure to know it. They always know what people are related. That's all they have to think about. But maybe they won't remember it if they don't want to. But if they want to, they will surely remember it. And that makes it worse for you. Why can't you leave women alone, Kini, little brother? Look at me, I have no troubles like that. I know very well that a man can't be a hunter, and fool with women at the same time, at least not let them get into his heart. My Weasel wouldn't like it. He would be jealous. And you, you who want to hunt bears, you make love to the wife of a sorcerer, granddaughter of another sorcerer, the most powerful one in the tribe, and your own blood relation. I tell you I wish you were all Indian. You wouldn't be such a fool, then. At least, why don't you offer to pay him back the marriage gifts?"

"Of course, I will!" cried Ruiz, "I will give him twice as much as he gave for her."

Pawi was silent for awhile. Then he said: "Maybe he will take it, and maybe he won't. I don't know. He is a strange fellow, that young sorcerer, just as strange as his name, Ne-sia-Hualala, 'I-will-cry.' What a name to give a child! His father used to be a sorcerer too. But I have never seen anybody perform like him. I didn't like his songs. They always made me feel queer. But he was a fine man and everybody liked him. He was good looking, too. And so was Hualala's mother. It is funny they should have made a child as ugly as he is. Maybe that's why they called him that name, to warn him that he would be unhappy. Well, he is unhappy enough right now. He was crazy about that woman of his. And now he is gone wandering. He started wandering towards the end of last moon. I think he must have lost his shadow. I have come upon him several times in the brush, singing and crying, breaking branches and throwing rocks about, and dancing in the bottoms of the canyons. Well, you know how a man acts when he starts to wander. It made me awfully sad to see him like that, and I tried to catch him and bring him back to the village. I thought the old blind man might go to work on him and bring his shadow back before it is too late. But he threw rocks at me and ran away."

Both men lapsed into silent contemplation of the sea way down below them and stretching far away to the west, calm and purple with a trail of copper from the sun.

Suddenly, a wild song broke from the woods below them on the other side of the ridge, and both men jumped to their feet. The song stopped as suddenly as it had commenced. There was a silence, then a series of incoherent shouts and the noise of snapping branches.

"There he goes, that's he," said Pawi, and he added: "Oh, it makes my heart sick."

There was silence again. Ruiz said, "It makes my heart sick, too. Let's call him. Maybe he will come." And he let out a calling yell: "Yllla-a-a-ay-ha! Iyo-o-o, Hualala iyo, miitz iyo! Come Hualala, come my brother!"

There was an answering yell from the woods. Then silence again. "There, he is coming all right, I hear him coming up. Call again."

A man emerged from the woods onto the trail at a short distance from where they were, and stood there hesitating for a moment. Then he saw them and came their way. He had a rumbling, heavy sort of gait, almost a shamble, and yet with something catlike about it. He was a hunchback with long swinging arms. His face was almost hideous, with one eye gone, and the other red from crying, a huge mouth full of pain, and a wild mass of hair, very long and tangled. He stopped in front of them and started to dance and sing. Then he stopped and sat on his heels, looking at the setting sun. He said: "Well, what do you fellows want, you called me and I came. If you want a doctor, then it's no use, because I have lost my power. I have no power now. I had lots of power, but now it's gone. But I know you two fellows. I know who you are. You are Pawi-maliay-hapa, and that's your brother, the man who stole my woman."

"No I did not, Hualala, you know I did not do that."

"That's right. You didn't do it. It wasn't your fault. I have nothing against you. If anybody says I am going to kill you, it is not true. You can't help it if you are in love with her. I know what it is, I who am her husband. She was so beautiful! She was my power. Now she is gone and she has taken my power away. I have no more power. I could not kill you even if I wanted to. But why should I want to kill you? Because you love her? You can't help that. You did not take her away. She went away herself. I have nothing against you. You can have her for your woman. She is all right. She is a fine woman for a man."

He sat looking at the setting sun. In spite of all his ugliness there was beauty in his face. It was full of malice, and full as well of gentleness. At the moment it was drowned in sorrow.

"Listen, Hualala," said Kinikilali, "Why don't you let me buy her from you? What's the good worrying about her. She loved you too, but she was afraid of you. She was afraid of your power. A sorcerer should not have a wife, no more than a hunter. Let me buy her from you. I will give you twice what you gave for her."

"I don't want anything for her," said the young sorcerer quietly. "I tell you, you can have her as a gift. I don't want anything. I can get all I want with my doctoring, if that was what I wanted."

"Don't be silly, Hualala. Listen, I will give you a horse, and show you how to ride, I don't care what the white men say!"

But Hualala flew into a passion. "What do I want a horse for? Am I not ugly enough without showing it to all the world, sitting on top of a horse!"

When he was quiet again he began to cry. "We had a beautiful baby. I am so ugly, but he was a beautiful child. Everybody said to me, 'I like your child.' But she killed it. She says I killed it with my power, but that's not true. She killed it, she killed it by not loving anymore. She didn't love me anymore. How could the child live after that, when it was my child, the child of my love. She took away her love, she took away my power. Of course the child died. My father used to say to me: 'Look at your mother and me, look at us, we have always been happy. That's because we love each other. We don't go fooling around like so many other people. That's the way to do it. You love the woman you buy. She has bought you also. She will love you, and your child will grow. That's the way to do it.' That is what my father used to say. But he gave me the wrong name. He could not help that. He used to say: 'You do what is right and your child will grow straight like a tree.' I guess he loved me so hard that he didn't see I was all crooked already."

The young shaman began to cry again. Ruiz-Kinikilali cinched his horse and started down the ridge. Pawi went down the other way, towards the Indian rancheria.

Ne-sia-Hualala remained alone, gazing at the setting sun. It was almost in the water, now, huge and red. Hualala looked and looked through his tears. He saw his mother, there in the sun. She had her pack-basket on her back and she was digging for roots, there in the red, huge sun. She did not go out of its circle, but was going further and further away, towards the center, getting smaller and smaller. Once she turned around and looked at him. Her face grew very large, as big as the whole son, and then she disappeared.

Then he saw his father. He was dancing and singing, right on top of the sun. Hualala could hear the song. It was one of his father's most powerful medicine songs, a song to call back the shadow when it is lost. He saw his father, still singing and dancing, jump into the circle of the sun, and he went away still singing and dancing, getting smaller and smaller, toward the center, and then he disappeared, but he never turned back his head. After he was gone, Hualala saw a little boy standing on top of the sun, right where his father had been. He was playing with a little bow and arrows. He was shooting them towards the water. When he had shot them all, he jumped into the circle of the sun and went away like the other two.

Ne-sia-Hualala sat there looking at the setting sun. He did not see anything else. The sun was half in the water. Now the sun was all gone, and there was the sudden chill of evening. Hualala shuddered. Then he knew that he had seen his own shadow. Then he knew that he was going to die.

He got up and hurried down the trail towards the Indian village. When he arrived there, he went straight to the ceremonial house, climbed to the roof and went down the centerpost ladder. It was full of men inside, sitting against the walls, listening to the recital of an ancient tale by Amomuths, the old blind sorcerer. His voice went on and on, monotonously.

Hualala went straight to a pile of bearskins and lay down with his face to the wall. Soon, all the men began to leave silently. They climbed up the ladder, pushed aside the flap over the smoke-hole and went off. You could hear their feet over the roof.

Very soon the old blind man and the young shaman were the only ones left in the ceremonial house. The fire was dying down. The old man kept telling his tale, monotonously, on and on, a long, long tale. When he had finished, he sat in silence for a while. Then he commenced singing a medicine song. It was a shadow calling-back song. He sang for a long time. Then he was silent again. Then he said: "Hey! Hualala! Hey! Ne-sia-Hualala, do you remember that calling-back song of your father's?"

"No, I don't remember it, little grandfather, that was a hard song and he took it away with him."

"That's too bad!" said the old man, and he lay down to sleep.

5
Fray Luis walks into the Trap & makes his Bargain with the Devil

Old Saturnino sat in the sun of the courtyard weaving a reata. In the sultriness of the afternoon there were only the small sounds of inactivity. The old Mayordomo sat weaving the strands of rawhide carefully, methodically, thinking nothing. Then a confused noise in the distance, coming from the valley, the bellowing of cattle, a cloud of dust rising in the air, the vaqueros' yells, and then creeping down over a slope the Mission herd came into view, with a dozen Indians running afoot on either side and behind, and Ruiz-Kinikilali, darting everywhere on his horse, shouting commands, cracking his long whip. Old Saturnino ceased weaving for a moment, watching with his mind full of bitterness.

He hated all the Esselens, and Kinikilali particularly. The young vaquero was a tease, and he liked to torment the old mayordomo whom all the Indians of the Mission feared. He affected to speak of him in the Esselen tongue. "I don't understand that jargon!" the old man would grumble. "Oh! but you ought to learn it, little grandfather, you are not too old yet. I can teach you if you like. Listen, you repeat after me: 'I am an old renegade, I am a mangy old coyote, I am *this* and I am *that*,'" *this* and *that* being the two most obscene epithets in the Esselen tongue. The old man only grumbled obstinately: "I don't understand your jargon!"

Saturnino stopped plaiting the strands of rawhide, while he watched the Mission herd and the vaqueros spreading down the side of the valley. Then he resumed his work, waiting for his tormentor.

Now the herd is in the corrals. The gate of the Mission patio swings open. Ruiz dashes in with a gay yell, up to a hitching post, with a swirl and a clatter. The Indians at work making adobes in a corner of the courtyard look up. Some smile, some of them just look with open mouth. Fray Bernardo comes out of his cell, with his eyes full of sleep and a scowl on his face, stands in the doorway a moment, shakes his head, smiles and goes in again. Fray Luis, pacing up and down the arcade, was telling his beads and never turned his head.

But this time Ruiz-Kinikilali was not in a teasing mood. Or perhaps it was that his vaquero's eye, full of thoughts about that bear at the Spring of the Fallen Madronyo, fell in love with the tightly woven reata in the hands of the old mayordomo. So he came over to him, and squatted on his heels and spoke softly, in Spanish: "Little grandfather! That's my reata, isn't it!" he begged. Saturnino looked up in sheer amazement. His jaw dropped. "Go to the devil! You . . . you, Oh! you go to the devil! . . . for you, this reata for you, for you?"

"Oh, for heaven's sake, don't be spiteful, old miser! Can't you take a joke? I don't care a damn whether you are an Esselen witch or a Rumsen apostate, or the head mumbler for the padres! I was just teasing you, that's all. I don't know what you did, except that you killed that woman, and what do I care! She was no relative of mine. Go back or don't go back, just as you like. I don't know what you did. Honestly I don't. They have told me, but I get it all mixed up. Only I don't like it the way you act, denying your own blood, and lording it over us! And anyhow, I won't tease you any more if you give me that reata. Come on now, little grandfather, don't be mean, give me that reata. I want it to get a bear. I must have a reata I can depend upon. You just finish this one for me, and I'll bring you all the bear grease you want. I know you are a bear magician. Oh! what's the use saying no. I don't talk that talk to the padres. I will bring you all the bear grease you want!"

Saturnino did not answer. He never lifted his eyes from the reata. He kept on plaiting the strands of rawhide, desperately. His hands were trembling. He knew he would have to undo all that work, loose plaiting, twisted, not good.

Fray Luis was pacing up and down the arcade, telling his beads.

"Come now, little grandfather, don't be mean! I want that reata. It's just the kind of reata I need. Hold any bear with it. Nobody like you to make a reata, little grandfather!"

Saturnino did not answer. He never lifted his eyes. His hands were trembling. He could not see them very well. He could not think. He went on plaiting desperately. There was something inside of him that tried to work, and would not work, only jerked and hurt, like a cramped muscle. Years and years of pain, of hatred. Hatred of the padres, hatred of the Esselens, hatred of the Rumsens, hatred of a courtyard filled with sun, each day, each day plaiting strands of rawhide, while the breakers boomed on the beach, over there on the other side of the wall. Hatred, memories, years of it, listening in the winter nights to the stormy winds from the south. Cut off from his power. Teaching prayers in Spanish to the neophytes! And now, a little snarling dog biting his legs, little snarling puppy begging a reata, puppy, mongrel puppy daring to tease him, him an old bear doctor, a powerful doctor, that's what he had been.

"Come, little grandfather, don't be mean, you finish that reata for me. Tell me you will. I shan't tease you anymore!"

Saturnino did not answer. He kept on plaiting. Fray Luis was still pacing up and down. The Indians who were making adobes struck up a song. Saturnino felt something bitter like gall spread throughout his whole body. He thought: "That's my power, he will come tonight." He kept on plaiting.

Now Fray Luis has finished his rosary. He hangs it in the monk's cord at his waist. He leaves the arcade. He crosses the patio.

Ruiz-Kinikilali stood up with a curse. He muttered in the Esselen tongue: "There comes the other fox, now, strutting with his tail over his head! All right, you old stubborn piece of rotting meat, I am going now. I want that reata, and I am going to have it, and you had better make it good and strong, otherwise I will . . ." Fray Luis was now quite close. The young vaquero strode off, nonchalantly.

Fray Luis seemed lost in thought. He stopped in front of the old mayordomo, watching his hands absently. Then he sat down beside the old man.

"Saturnino," he began, "they say that you know more about the old pagan ways than any other of the old men around here. Tell me something that I have been thinking about. . . . Hey! Saturnino! Listen to me. Are you awake or asleep? I believe you do weave in your sleep!"

"No, Your Reverence, I am not asleep. I am listening. Only I wish you wouldn't ask me those questions. And anyhow, why do you want to know about all those bad things? Look at the good Fray Bernardo. He does not bother his head about the pagan customs. He is a good padre. But you, you are too curious of those bad things. Go and ask the other old men. Don't ask me. I don't think it is right of you!"

Fray Luis laughed: "Excuse me, Don Saturnino, and thank you for the lecture. But do not worry. My motives are excellent. We must all learn about the ways of the Devil in order the better to combat him. And as for the other old men, I have already asked them, but they all say that you know more than anybody else."

"Nonsense!" grumbled the old man. He looked at the reata in his hands, puzzling. He began to unplait the strands of rawhide.

"What are you doing?" asked the monk.

"Well, this work is no good. Have to do it over again. That dirty little mongrel came here to make me angry, and I got angry inside, and I spoiled this part. See, look how it's all crooked. You see, Padre, you must have peace inside to work right. Look at those strands, all crooked! And the very end of the reata, too. Almost finished. About two armlengths more. Damn that boy! And now what am I to do? Those strands will never plait straight again, not now that they have been twisted once. The end of the reata, too! You are not a vaquero, Don Luis, so you don't know what it means, but you see, this is the end they wrap around the horn of the saddle. Some say that the end of the reata near the honda is the most important part. But I say: Nonsense! Look at all the vaqueros who have a thumb missing. And where is that thumb? Cut off by the reata! Caught in the turns around the horn. Look at all the vaqueros with a limp. And why do they limp? End of the reata jammed around the horn. Can't turn Mr. Bull loose. Pulls down Mr. Horse. Mr. Vaquero under horse. Leg broken. And whose fault? Who made that reata? Old Saturnino! . . . No, no, Don Luis, you are not a vaquero but I can tell you that this end of the reata is the important end. And now, what am I going to do? I tell you these strands will never plait straight and tight again. . . . Oh, damn that conceited puppy! And what do you think, Fray Luis, but he had the impudence to ask me to give him this reata, to hunt bears, he said. Hunt bears! I hope the bear hunts him, and gets him, too!"

"Tche! tche!" reproved the monk. "You mustn't talk that way, little grandfather. You must not wish ill to anyone. . . . And, look, I may not be a vaquero, but still I can tell you something about that reata, about making a smooth end. . . ."

The old mayordomo looked at the monk dubiously. "How?" he asked.

"Plait it around a core. That will make the strands perfectly straight, and the reata even."

Saturnino smiled. "Yes, of course, Don Luis, I know that trick. But it's not nice. I know lots of people make reatas that way, plait the strands around a straight core. Of course it looks smooth and pretty . . . as long as it is new. But the core always stretches first before the plaited strands, and you get a kink, and that's where your reata is going to break. Still, I suppose I might . . ."

He looked again at the reata in his hands, absorbed in thought. Then he began to curse once more: "Damn that mongrel! I hope he dies! I don't care what you say, Padre, that boy is bad. He is an Esselen anyhow. They are all like that, in his tribe, bad people, witches! You yourself, you don't like him, you know very well you don't like him. Why don't you get rid of him? What's the use of your being a priest then? Our priests, they know how to kill people. You ought to be able to make him die. What's the use of your knowing so many prayers, then? I would kill him myself, but I can't seem to do it! You see, half of him is white. Indian medicine does not seem to catch hold on white men. . . ."

The old man worked himself into a fury, and then quickly subsided again, and now he sat brooding, looking at the reata in his hands, never noticing the amazement and horror on the monk's face. In a corner of the patio, several Indians were mixing mud and straw for adobes. They were singing an endless tune. The afternoon was very quiet. Sky very blue overhead. Fray Bernardo came out of his room, drew a chair near the edge of the arcade to get a better light, and began reading his breviary. A cart came in through the gate, loaded with firewood. The driver sat on the tongue, half asleep, goading the oxen mechanically. The cart wheels made a screeching noise. At last, Fray Luis found his voice. But it was a mere whisper, a hoarse whisper: "Saturnino, Saturnino, are you crazy? What's happened to you? What's the matter with you? What do you mean?"

The old mayordomo snapped back: "Nothing is the matter with me, Your Reverence! And you know very well what I mean.

So why scold me? That boy is going to take your girl away, and you hate him as much as I do, and you know it!"

"I don't understand what you are talking about, Saturnino, I think you are crazy. Sitting here in the sun all day . . ."

"Crazy nothing! He has had her already, or I am a fool! She wasn't in the nunnery the other night. She was there all right in the evening, when I locked them up, but she was not there in the morning. I told Fray Bernardo. But all he said was: Don't bother me this morning! If we don't get a permit from the Comandante we can't buy anything from the ship that has just come into the harbor from the Philippines, and we have only fifty fanegas of wheat left, and they are full of rice on board, and you talk to me about a puta who slept out of her bed last night! That's the way he talked to me. Well, where was she? Was she with you, eh?"

"Silence! you insolent fool, you insolent old fool! Do you want to get the lash, you the mayordomo?"

"Go ahead, Don Luis, I don't care! Won't be the first time! Remind me of the old days. But that won't give her back to you!"

"Listen, you old imbecile, listen with both your ears: we, the priests, have no intercourse with women!"

"Well, maybe you don't yourself, but all the other padres do! What's wrong with you, Don Luis? Are you a coya?"

The old man's voice was so full of suspicion that Fray Luis' anger subsided and he burst into laughter.

Seeing the tension relieved, Saturnino grumbled: "Give me your cord, Your Reverence, please."

"Eh! my what?"

"Your cord, please, your cord, that rope around your waist!"

"But what for, what do you want my cord for? I need it myself!"

"I want it for this reata here, Your Reverence, it will make a good core. You gave me the idea yourself."

"I think you are a lunatic, Saturnino. Well, here, take it. You are an old fool. You shouldn't sit so long in the sun. Addle your brains. Poor old fellow . . . !"

The adoberos were still singing their morose tune. Fray Bernardo whisked over the pages. The sun was near the edge of the wall.

6
The unholy
Partnership begins

Old Esteban sat on his stump, in the afternoon sun, watching the ocean below. He heard the corral gate screech, then footsteps around the corner of the house, then footsteps inside the house, then the door behind him opened, and he knew without turning the tall young form in the doorway. He said: "Little son, you have been away a long time, I have missed you!"

"I couldn't help it, Sir. The fathers had a lot of cattle to bring in for branding, and you know, I am chief of the vaqueros, I am now for sure, Fray Bernardo told me. . . ."

"Ah! yes, very good, it is well, it is well." The old man's voice trailed off. His eyes roamed over the sparkling expanse of water, looking for a sail. Then he spoke again.

"Somebody died over there, on the other side of the ridge, in the rancheria, while you were gone. I heard them crying for several nights. They have been wailing for several nights. I wonder who it was. Maybe some relative of your mother. I am glad you have come back."

"I think I know who it was, Father."

"Ah!" said the old man, and his eye roved over the glittering ocean.

He stayed there till sunset, looking over the lonely sea at the foot of the lonely hills, then he shivered with the coming dusk and went inside the house. Ruiz had fried some venison. The old man ate in silence. Then he stretched himself in his blankets against the wall, singing an old tune under his breath, an old malaguena. After a time he fell asleep. Ruiz had gone. It was all silent in the house.

All silent, save for a cricket, several mice, and a very active pack-rat who was trying to bully them. Through the open door the moonlight came in. The mice were busy, storing grains of wheat in a nest where the last rafter met the roofsill. They stole the wheat from an open wicker basket in the corner at the foot of the old man's bed of blankets, then they crossed the patch of moonlight in front of the open door, and then they jumped onto a box, from there onto the table, and from there scrambled up the corner of the wall to their nest. The pack-rat had a hoard on a shelf behind the sea-chest. At present he was trying to take an onion there. His path ran along a tie in the wall as far as an upright, then through a knothole in the upright, and along another tie, and then onto the shelf. Unfortunately the knothole was too small for the onion. So the pack-rat would turn around, back into the knothole and the onion would be jerked out of his mouth and roll onto the floor. He tried it again and again, stubbornly, and ever time he had a chance he bullied the mice as they crossed the patch of moonlight in front of the door, while old Esteban snored and the cricket sang in a corner of the chimney.

The cricket sang: "Tse-dze, tse-dze, tsee-dze-dze! They are crying over there. The night is still, but they are crying over there. Tse-dze! tsee-dze-dze! Some people die, but the crickets never die. . . ."

The pack-rat stopped in the middle of the floor: "Well! I'll be damned. . . ." He addressed the room at large, ignoring the mice: "Some people think they have power, they sing, yes, they sing, well . . . I could sing too if I wanted to, if I were not so busy. What's the matter with this thing, anyhow? Hey, you Mr. Mouse, shut up, why can't you be polite, and listen to this fellow's song. He is a good doctor, that's a good song, better listen to it!"

MOUSE: "I didn't say anything!"

PACK-RAT: "Shut up!"

CRICKET: "Tse-dze, tse-dze, tsee-dze, somebody's dead, somebody's dead, somebody's dead!"

PACK-RAT: "How do you know somebody is dead? Lots of people die. Who is dead, anyhow?"

CRICKET: "He had power! His own power killed him, tse-dze, tse-dze, tsee-dze-dze!!"

PACK-RAT: "Aw! shut up, you make me sad. What's the matter with you? Why don't you help me with this crazy thing? . . . There it goes again!"

MOUSE: "Hush everybody! . . . Someone is coming. . . ."

Silence in the house. The snoring of Esteban.

A VOICE OUTSIDE: "Ave Maria purisima! Senores! . . . Paz en esta casa! Por el amor de Dios, dispiertense! Wake up, wake up, and give asylum to a priest!"

ESTEBAN: "A la Virgen Purisima! Who speaks my tongue . . ."

Old Esteban scrambles out of his blankets, dizzy with sleep, out into the moonlight. There stands Fray Luis, tall, thin, austere, a dead pine-tree, with his two eyes burning.

ESTEBAN: "Where the devil do you come from? Your voice . . . your accent . . ."

FRAY LUIS: "I have been calling for a half-hour! Go and put

my mule in your stable, and feed him! Where is your son?"

ESTEBAN: "Your Reverence, my Lord, I do not know. Somebody died on the other side of the ridge, and he went up. . . . What is it that you want to know, and why do you come at this hour?"

FRAY LUIS: "You live in an infernal sort of place! . . . Well, saddle me a horse!"

ESTEBAN: "Saddle you a horse, saddle you a horse!!!! Catch the horse, Your Reverence, and the more luck to you, and be bucked to hell! Who are you anyway? This is your house, and every man and beast is yours, my handsome Lord in your brown skirts, I'll bring you my very best bronco, take off your skirts and ride him, ride him to the hills and to the other side and see for yourself then!"

The two men stood in the moonlight, eyeing each other insolently for a minute. Then the old soldier shuffled away toward the corrals. Soon he came back leading a snorting horse.

"Here, Your Reverence, hold him while I throw my saddle on him. He is young and quick, and a bit snorty, but he won't buck."

"Hurry up, hurry up, old man!"

"But why so much hurry? There is time for everything in this world."

"No, time is short! Death is always around the corner!"

The monk twisted the cassock around his waist and leaped into the saddle. Before starting he turned to Esteban: "You say that the trail is straight over the ridge?"

"Yes, right straight over the ridge and down. You won't have any trouble finding the Indian rancheria. They are holding a funeral dance for somebody who died and you will see the fire long before you get there, and you will hear them singing."

Horse and friar were panting up the trail. The moon made the ocean sparkle. On either side of the trail there was a thin mist in the bottoms of the canyons. It rose in curly wisps hugging the slopes, and vanished in the warmer air. Fear was creeping into Fray Luis' heart, and he urged the horse. They paused at last on top of the ridge. A long, lithe, tawny form leaped away and vanished without a sound. A night-hawk boomed close to the monk's head. The horse was panting fast. Fray Luis could feel his own heart beating into his ears. He looked down into the canyon on the outer side of the ridge. Way down below he saw the flare of a fire. Then a waft of wind carried to him for an instant the booming sound of the drum. Fray Luis and his horse started down the trail.

Down in the canyon, at the Indian village on the flat, in the moonlight, they were holding the funeral dance for Hualala. From many throats came the song, deep male voices, high pitched notes from the women, a monotonous dirge with strongly marked accents, and a stamping of feet in rhythm.

He-e, hi yan-hiayan, hee . . . and feet stamping and a whole line of dancers moving as one man, swaying, moving slowly in sideways steps, slowly going around the fire . . . he hiam-hee. . . . And according to the ancient custom, in the ceremonial-house, alone, lay a girl, the handsomest, ready for the stranger, for any who might come. . . .

A VOICE FROM THE TRAIL: "Hermanos! Peace be to this camp!"

KINIKILALI: "Kill him!"

The dance of the mourners has stopped. There is a moment of indecision, while the fire crackles and the trees are illumined. Several men with their hair cropped and their faces smeared with pitch have seized the monk. In the silence Fray Luis' horse whinnies in the darkness outside, then starts home with a clatter of hoofs crossing the boulders of the creek.

FRAY LUIS: "Lord, my God, this is my time, thy will be done!"

THE OLD BLIND DOCTOR: "Who is the stranger?"

KINIKILALI: "A white priest. Kill him."

THE OLD BLIND DOCTOR: "Silence! What do you know! It never was that a stranger was killed at a death dance. Don't I know the way it always was? Take the stranger to the ceremonial-house. The woman is there waiting. Let the stranger take the burden of death from us. That's the way it always was."

An old woman with her hair cropped and her face smeared with pitch jumps on the monk and executes an obscene mimicry before him. Shouts of ribald laughter. The monk is roughly dragged and pushed to the roof of the ceremonial-house. Shoved through the smoke-hole, with laughter, as he scrambles down the center-post ladder, into the darkness within, and the deerskin flap is pulled over again.

More sticks to the fire. The funeral pyre grows. Tongues of flame leap up curling with dense smoke. An inert body is thrown on top. The old woman sets up the piercing mourning wail, curling high through the night. Other women join. The mourning chant rises again, with the stamping of feet, around and around ..

....

Old Esteban tried to go back to sleep. Then he got up muttering. He saddled his horse, and started up the ridge............................

The onion rolled onto the floor again for the hundredth time. The mice went on stealing wheat. The cricket sang: "They are burning him at last. He would have been a fine doctor, but his own power killed him. Tse-dze, tsee-dze-dze! Crickets don't die. They live forever like the fire!"

A MOUSE, stopping on his way across the patch of moonlight: "I wonder who the stranger was. Queer looking chap. Never saw one like that before. Something nice about him. I am worried about him."

SECOND MOUSE: "Never mind about the stranger and pack your wheat! The night won't last forever!"

FIRST MOUSE: "Oh! keep quiet! Don't bother me! I wasn't talking to you anyway. You are just a common mouse. You have no power! You don't know anything about that kind. Pack your own wheat and let me alone. I took a fancy to that stranger. What do you think, Cricket? Shall I go and help him?"

CRICKET: Tse-dze, tse-dze, tsee-dze-dze! Lots of people die when they are not careful. A man must have a protector. That's the way it always was."

MOUSE: "I am worried about that stranger. Eh, Moon! Hey, Mr. Moon, I want to go up there!"

PACK-RAT: "Damn that thing!"

The Moon sends a ray. It comes through the air of night, like a long stick, right through the night towards the open door. It comes to rest on the floor of the cabin. The Mouse jumps on it. They go flying through the night, up, up, towards the mountain.

PACK-RAT: "Some fellows are lucky! I wish the Moon would help me with this damn thing!" ....

Fray Luis stayed nearly a week at the cabin of old Esteban. The old man liked him, liked to talk to him about the little pueblo of white-washed houses on the plains of La Mancha. He sang malaguenas, tangos and jotas, in a cracked voice. The monk listened. He was taciturn. They sat in front of the house, in the sun, watching the glittering ocean below. Fray Luis was taciturn and moody. Ruiz was riding the range, gathering stray cattle. He came in only in the evening. He stood in the doorway at their backs and said nothing. They ate venison and acorn soup. Then old Esteban would sing a jota or two and stretch himself on his bed of blankets. Ruiz would walk off to the corral without a word and saddle a fresh horse, and the friar would pace up and down in the moonlight in front of the house, for hours and hours. The nights were warm.

One night he took off his cassock and snatched a wildcat skin for a loin-cloth, and he started up the ridge. He was excited and feverish. He did not notice the mouse that followed him. He went up the trail fast. He was panting. He got to the top of the ridge. The whole world was bathed in moonlight. He saw a puma slink away in the moonlight. He said: "Brother! help me!" The puma turned his face once and Fray Luis saw the two green eyes for a second.

Fray Luis looked for the down trail. He went down for a score paces. Then he found a bifurcation into two trails. He was trying to remember. The mouse was running down the right trail excitedly and coming back. He would run a little way and come back, and run again, a little small thing, chip-chip-chipping in the mottled light through the trees. But Fray Luis was calling: "Oh, Puma, my brother, come and tell me!" He listened intently in the silence of the night. He was panting. He thought he heard a sound coming, coming. . . . He listened. . . . Jingle-jingle-jingle, the jingle of spurs, and the cadence of a horse's footfalls. Jingle-jingle-jingle, they passed by. Jingle-jingle-jingle, diminishing off in the distance..

7
Fray Luis Tries to Double-cross the Devil

What were the results of Fray Luis' journey down the Coast for the propagation of the faith? It is difficult to surmise.

He came back in a sullen mood and answered Fray Bernardo's anxious inquiries with ill grace. "They are the worst kind of wild savages, and we cannot do anything with them!" was all he would say, while the Catalan friar wisely nodded and answered: "Didn't I tell you so?"

On the other hand, if we turn to his diary we find nothing but an incoherent medley of prayers, invocations, appeals to all the Saints, and Martyrs, and Virgins of the calendar, mixed with shocking blasphemies and obscenities, showing that at the time his mind was deranged.

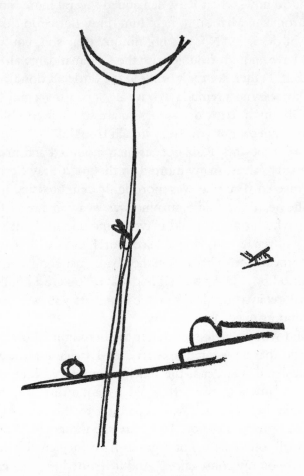

It was at about that time that Ruiz-Kinikilali also came back to the Mission. He rode every day. He was gathering the summer cattle. There were many new calves. It was very difficult to keep the different brands apart. Ruiz complained to Fray Bernardo that the new settlers on the Monterey side of the hill were letting their cattle drift towards the Carmel Valley. Already he had brought his cousin Pawi-maliay-hapa to help on horseback, and Fray Bernardo had winked at the breach of the rule against mounting an

Indian. So now, when Ruiz demanded several more mounted Indians from the Mission to help him, Fray Bernardo threw up his hands in despair: "No, no, no, no, my dear son, you cannot do that. I have enough trouble with the Commandante already!"

"But, Father, we can't bring in the cattle all alone, just two of us on horses, and a remuda of boys afoot panting a mile behind!"

"Oh, my son, my dear son, you are so much trouble! You are a good vaquero, but you are so much trouble!"

So, in the end, Ruiz got his men mounted and brought in a great many calves, many more than the good Fray Bernardo had ever expected. The friar was thoroughly delighted and happy, and when he heard that old Saturnino was weaving a reata for his pet vaquero, he blessed the old mayordomo and said with emotion: "God will repay you, you old scoundrel, God will repay you for your forbearance. That boy is not bad. Just foolish and young, but a good boy. Make him a good reata. You are a good old man, God will repay you. Make him the best reata you ever made!" And Saturnino grinned, sardonically.

And when a little while after the branding Ruiz said to Fray Bernardo that he wanted to marry the Esselen girl, now that her own husband was dead, the old friar embraced him with tears: "Yes, yes, my son, my little golden vaquero, marry her, that's right, take her for your wife according to the rules of our holy Church, I give her to you, I am sure she wants you. You take her back with you. This is not a good place for her. She has been a great care on my conscience!" And he trotted in great excitement to break the good news to Fray Luis.

Ruiz was crossing the courtyard. Saturnino called him. He threw the reata at him gruffly: "There you have it, and a good one it is! Now, be sure to bring me enough bear grease to pay for it."

"For me? Is it for me? Do you really mean it, little grandfather?"

Saturnino did not answer. He gathered his strands of rawhide and went back into the pozoleria. The vaquero shouted after him: "Thank you, grandfather. I will bring you all the grease you want! I'll get that bear now!"

He stood for a while slowly coiling and uncoiling the reata. He was running it through his fingers, amorously. Not a fault, not a kink, not a single uneven place. Like a snake, lithe, coiling and uncoiling. His eyes were large with pleasure. Then he caught sight of Pawi, at the other end of the courtyard, talking to several Indians. His manner changed. Mischief bubbled over him. He slid open the loop, he tiptoed to the group. The other Indians saw him but never betrayed it by even a wink. There was a hiss through the air, and a very small loop descended neatly over Pawi's head. He turned quickly, but his arms were already pinioned with a jerk. Ruiz-Kinikilali "sat" on the end of the reata and danced on one foot, all the while imitating the grunt of a bear. There were shouts of laughter all over the courtyard. Fray Bernardo came out of his cell to see what was the matter, and he laughed.

The sun was halfway down. The shadows were lengthening. A woman started a song in a high voice; behind one of the walls, Fray Luis was pacing up and down the northern arcade. Every time, as he approached the western end, more and more of his long and gaunt form cassocked in brown emerged into the light, up to his neck. But his head remained in the shadow. He turned slowly, and the golden light retreated down his body, till even his sandaled feet were lost in the penumbra. The late afternoon was windless. It was high tide, and from the beach, over there beyond the walls, came the boom of the breakers.

"Well, let's start for home," said Pawi.

"No, not yet, I don't want to go yet, brother, I want to see my girl, tonight."

"Oh! there you are again! Bad business! Well, I am not going to stay any longer."

"What are you afraid of, Pawi? You can go any time you want to. Nobody will stop you. They can't keep you here. You are not a convert. They can't make you stay here."

"I know, I know, Kini, but I don't like it here. I want to go home!"

"All right, very well, brother, go home, go home. I'll start myself in the morning, but I want to see my girl tonight!"

Pawi-maliay-hapa went over to his horse, the one his cousin had given him, and he straightened the saddle blankets. He tightened the cincha. He did everything conscientiously, the way Ruiz had taught him. He swung himself into the saddle. He said: "I wish you would start right now with me, brother."

But Ruiz only laughed: "If you had a girl here, you wouldn't be in such a hurry to go home. Never mind, I'll be there tomorrow and we'll get that bear! Go on now, metele, metele, vaquero!"

He slapped the horse on the haunch and threw up his arms with a yell. The horse was young, and had it not been for two weeks of daily riding, he would have bucked. As it was he only spurted away in a cloud of dust toward the gate. The Indian at his post there smiled, threw a greeting in Rumsen while he opened the gate hurriedly, and the Esselen vaquero passed out in a swirl of dust. The gates closed again.

The night was windless. The Mission was asleep. The girl slid over the wall, and Kinikilali caught her in his arms. She was panting with excitement. He kissed her for a long time. Then they slept in a tight embrace, lost in the moonlight, till the cold woke them. She sat up with a start. "I must go, Kini, little Both-ways, you my darling, Oh! it was good, Kini, I must go now, help me over the wall. . . ."

"Oh! wait, little Tickly-one, my sweetheart, let's have another!"

"No, Kini, I can't, I don't want another . . . yes, I would like it, but I am afraid. Listen, Kini, if I am caught, I'll get whipped again. I can't trust that old woman. She said that if I didn't come back before the moon goes down, she would go to sleep and lock the door of the nunnery. She is afraid of Saturnino. I can't help it. Don't be a fool. Do you want me to be whipped again? I only got ten lashes, but I will get the full twenty-five, this time. . . ."

"What are you talking about? Did you really get whipped?"

"Of course I did! Don't you suppose I would stay here all night with you, otherwise? Let me go! Please, darling! No, I don't want to. I tell you I shall get whipped, twenty-five times, yes, twenty-five times, do you want to take it for me?"

Ruiz-Kinikilali stood up in the moonlight, regardlessly. He was trembling. He said at last: "Who gave you the whipping? Did that monk do it?"

"No, the old woman did, the one who is in charge of us. . . ."

"Did it hurt?"

"Of course it hurt! Fray Luis was there watching. She was afraid of him, and she laid it on hard!"

Ruiz-Kinikilali was still trembling in the moonlight. He said: "All right, darling, come on, I'll help you over the wall, never mind, we will soon be out of here!"

She did not kiss him. She hesitated: "Kini, my little Bothways, please don't get into trouble!"

"I won't get into any trouble. Come on, darling, put your feet in my hands, that's right, now grab my hair, can you sit on the wall? All right, good adios, my little louse, my darling. . . ."

Ruiz-Kinikilali stood there in the shadow for a long time. Then he put his foot in a crack of the wall and vaulted over. He slunk along the wall noiselessly. He knew where the cell of Fray Luis was. He stood outside, in the shade of the arcade. He listened. He heard noises, voices, inside the room, a wild, insane idea came into his mind. He trembled again. Then he felt for the handle of the long blade in the folds of his sash.

He stood under the window of Fray Luis' cell. It was set high, just a little higher than his head. He heard voices inside, at least one voice, but he thought there were two. He could not reach the window. He grasped the ledge. His fingers blanched. He dropped down again. He unsheathed his knife and held it in his teeth. He looked around. He wanted a block of wood, something, anything to stand on. In the darkness of the arcade he could find nothing. He did not dare trust himself in the moonlight of the courtyard.

He grasped the window-ledge once more. With his fingertips blanched, he looked inside, he looked, he looked inside the cell of the monk.

He saw Fray Luis stark naked, utterly naked, with a whip in

his fist and alone. Alone, alone, he was, utterly alone he was, the flagellant in his cell, while the blood streaked down his back. And every time he switched the rawhide, every time he groaned, every time he shuddered and begged the Saints for their mercy. And the blood streamed down the back, red, red, impossibly red.

Ruiz-Kinikilali let his fingers go off the window ledge. He sank to the ground. His mind was reeling. He himself reeled across the courtyard, full in the moonlight. He did not care. He stood there in the middle of the patio, and he vomited. Then he turned towards the chapel. He found the door. He opened it. He went inside. The sacramental light burned, quietly, evenly, soothingly. Ruiz-Kinikilali did not understand, but he prayed. . . . He prayed, he prayed, and prayed, fervently. He prayed as he stood crouching in the shadow of the pillar: "God Almighty, my Father, my own Father, save me, save me from the Devil, from Him whom I have just seen, my Father, my Father come to me!" Everything reeled before his eyes. A whip lashing through the air. The flesh of a woman, and streaks of red over white. . . . Then silence and darkness for a long time..

The door of the Church creaked on its hinges, and the two monks came in for Matins. Fray Luis carried an oil lamp. Fray Bernardo swayed with sleep. Fray Luis lit the tapers. They stood, facing each other across the nave. Fray Luis intoned in a sonorous voice. Fray Bernardo responded, his voice heavy with sleep. Back and forth, back and forth in the hollowness of the chapel. Till the end of Matins. Fray Bernardo put out the tapers. The door grated on its hinges, and closed with a bang. Silence.

Ruiz-Kinikilali shuddered. He looked at the sacramental light. Why should it be red, like blood? He shuddered. He crept to the door, out into the coolness of the night. His horse was tied at the hitching-post.

Jingle-jingle-jingle, the cadence of spurs . . . Fray Luis turns on his couch and mutters. Jingle-jingle-jingle . . . off, away, down the road in the moonlight.

Fray Luis is tossing about on the planks of his bed. He dreams. He mumbles and moans. He tosses about restlessly and the rough cassock, stiff with blood, tears at the stripes on his back. He moans, while the monsters of the night surge about him in his nightmare. He hears the jingle of spurs. It is dark where he is, and way down there, there is something he must reach, some meeting he must attend. The jingle of spurs in the dark. No, nothing, silence. He must go down there, down the steep trail, dark, dark, in utter blackness, waiting for someone, waiting for her who will lead the way. Ah! there she stands, the black woman, the black virgin, waiting for him by the side of the trail, utterly black in the blackness, she who said: "Nigra sum, sed formosa!" She leads the way down, down, down the dark trail, for a long, for an interminable time. At last they come to the creek. It is a swollen torrent. It must have been raining. She lifts him in her arms. She wades through the water. He clings to her in his fear. There are many people, crowds of people standing in the village in among the huts. Suddenly they all vanish. All is deserted, ominously silent. Still carrying him in her arms, the black virgin, she wends her way in and out of the conical huts (there were thousands and thousands of them). They arrive at the ceremonial-house, large, immense, looming up to the sky. Up to the roof they go, up, climbing to the top of the world. They stand on the roof. He, very small, clings to her, trembling, afraid of her. Down through the smoke-hole they go, down the center-post ladder. Now they stand in the middle of the floor, and all around the wall they are seated, all of them silent, impassive. They begin to chant the mourning song. The black woman has disappeared. He stands there in the middle of the floor, at the foot of the centerpost ladder. They chant. For whom are they chanting? Are they chanting for himself? Is this himself, laid there dead across the fire? Or is it the young half-breed vaquero? When did he die? They are chanting, chanting, chanting the death-song, interminably. Will they ever stop? Why must he stand thus in the middle, without a breech-clout, while they sing around the wall, and the other one burns? He will speak, he will ask for fair judgment. They know it. They stop the chant. He opens his mouth. Vainly, vainly, he opens his mouth. Soundless, speechless, utterly impotent. Why, but why? What is this feeling, abominable, creeping up, up his legs, insistent, anxious, creeping, snatching, gripping, grasping, tearing off, tearing them off, my God! . . .

The yell sounded through the dawn. Fray Luis lay quivering on the planks of his bed. The first ray of the morning sun came through the high barred window and rested on the opposite wall. A cock crowed. An Indian was yoking the oxen to his cart in the patio: "Hoy! Hoy! hoy! aee! hoy!" ....

8
The Devil carries out
his Bargain

Ruiz and his cousin sat in their saddles, in the shadow, at the edge of the little flat where the carcass of a young bull lay, half-devoured, still fresh. It was near the end of the moon, and not much light. They fidgeted in their saddles, in utter silence, shifting from side to side, reatas unslung and the loop trailing to the ground. They dozed and started, and dozed and started, and dozed again. The crackling of a twig, and they sat up in their saddles, utterly awake, impossibly awake, on the very edge of intentness. . . . Silence for a long time. Maybe the bear had smelled them and gone away. . . . Then the crunching of bones . . . Kinikilali leaned away over in his saddle and placed his lips right into Pawi's ear, so that it tickled him. "Drop your reata! Get an arrow ready. I'll surely get him the way he is placed, and I'll drag him to the south. Get off and shoot while I drag him. All right? All right! Wait . . . Ahora!!" And with a yell he rushed his horse in the open. He was left-handed, and as he turned, he swung the loop right over the bear's uplifted head in wonder, and without stopping he circled to the south.

He expected a jerk on the reata, although perhaps not quite such an uncompromising one. The well trained horse swirled on his forefeet and sat on his haunches. Pawi was there, in the moonlight, just exactly where he was to be. The short, hard bow was drawn way back. The release, and the hum of the string. Almost immediately another arrow. Then another, and a fourth one. Then Pawi stood looking, in the uncertain moonlight, mouth half-opened, with his bow still lifted, with his right arm still drawn back. He had seen every one of the arrows bounce back. And now he was watching the bear drawing in on the reata, arm over arm, slowly, leisurely. At the other end of the reata the horse was plunging frantically.

"Turn him loose, Kini, turn him loose, quick!"

What was the matter with Kinikilali? He was fumbling with the turns of the reata on the horn of his saddle. He yelled: "I am jammed! Shoot him again for heaven's sake!"

Two more arrows. They bounced back.

Down went the horse, on his knees, and Ruiz-Kinikilali tumbled over the horn.

Just a rip of the paw. Then the bear started up the hill, dragging the horse for a few paces, until the reata snapped, near the horn of the saddle.

The bear was climbing up, slowly, leisurely, in the half-moonlight, towards the ridge, dragging the reata. . . .

9
And begins
to demand his Price

Esteban sat on his stump looking over the ocean, looking for a sail. After a while he was dimly conscious of someone standing over him. He brought himself to reality with an effort. "What is it, Pawi-maliay-hapa?"

"Kinikilali is dead. The bear killed him."

Esteban's eye roamed again over the glittering ocean. At last he said: "Did he walk away with the reata?"

"Yes."

Esteban sat on his stump looking over the ocean, silent for a long time. Pawi-maliay-hapa stood in silence waiting. Finally Esteban tried to get up. Then he said crossly: 'Help me, you!"

They went slowly towards the corrals. "Catch me that horse! No, not that one, this one here, there . . . bueno . . . saddle him."

Slowly they rode up the trail, slowly, slowly, because the old man, and he was in the lead, stopped so often and let his head drop, while his horse ate the grasses. But at last they were over the ridge, and Esteban Berenda led the way down the trail, down to the rancheria, and he stayed there a long time with Amomuths, the old blind sorcerer...

Fray Bernardo took the news badly, at the Mission, when Pawi came. He wrung his hands and cried and lamented. The adoberos knew already. They had known since the morning of that day, and nobody struck up a song that day, nor for several days thereafter. There was a pall of silence over the Mission. Saturnino sat in the sun in front of his pozoleria, weaving reatas as usual. He was listening intently to the talk between Fray Bernardo and Pawi-maliay-hapa, carried on through an interpreter. Pawi said the Esselens wanted the girl to be returned to them. Fray Bernardo tried to explain that now she had been baptized and was a Christian, she could not leave the Mission any more. Pawi would listen politely, and then repeat his stubborn request: "The old men want her to come back." Until Fray Bernardo went away in despair. He went to see Fray Luis.

"Here, you know their language, and you have been there. Try to make him understand. I don't want any trouble. My God! I only wish the girl were away from here, but it is against the rules, it is against the rules, I cannot do it, I cannot do it. Now, you try to make him understand. These people seem different from our Indians. He just stands there like an idiot, and repeats the same thing over and over again: the old men want her to come back! To the devil with their old men! I can't help it! Fray Luis, do you try to talk to him, please!"

And so Fray Luis crossed over to where Pawi-maliay-hapa stood, and spoke to him. But Pawi only looked and never answered, never gave the least sign of comprehension. Fray Luis then made the interpreter repeat what he himself had just said.

But Pawi stood there, dumb. Fray Luis reddened and turned back. Saturnino was bending over his reata. Then Pawi went over to him and spoke quickly, in an undertone. Saturnino gave no sign of having understood. Pawi turned and went over to his horse and untied him. He climbed into the saddle slowly. He passed out of the yard slowly. The Indian at the gate opened it, but called no greeting. He closed the gate again ....

Fray Luis stopped in front of the old mayordomo, where he sat in the sun, in front of his pozoleria, weaving reatas. "Saturnino, what's the matter with everybody around here? One would think I am a leper! I am not blind, I can see it! All the old fellows who used to talk to me, they act now as if they were dumb, and deaf. What's the matter? What's the matter?"

Saturnino stopped weaving a moment. Without lifting his head, he said: "I don't know. Who can tell what's the matter with the old imbeciles, they are so old, some of them. . . . But, listen, Fray Luis, you had better send the girl back!"

"What are you talking about, Saturnino?"

"I say that you must send the girl back."

"But what have I to do with it? Tell this to Fray Bernardo. He has charge of this Mission. . . . Anyway, it is useless. You know yourself very well that she can not leave the Mission now that she is a Christian."

"Look here, Fray Luis, I don't want to argue with you. . . . The girl must go back there, otherwise you and I will pay!"

"Look here, you old addle-brained fool, I don't understand what it is that you are talking about. I am tired of you, and of that girl, and of the Rumsens, and of the Esselenes, and of the whole damn thing!"

And Fray Luis turned away and began pacing up and down the arcade. Saturnino went on weaving reatas...........................
....

A few days later the Esselen girl disappeared, and Saturnino reported the matter to Fray Bernardo. . . .

Fray Luis wrote in his diary: "Wednesday. Feast of San

Geronimo. Nothing has happened today, except that the little Es-selen girl has gone. Escaped to her wild home probably. Good riddance, thinks Father Tallow, but it makes me horribly sad. I hear the pounding of the breakers on the beach and it makes me think of her, I don't know why. May God allow that they treat her well, there. I baptized her with my own hands. My one and only Esselen convert! I feel tired and discouraged, these days. I would like to escape too, run away to the wild hills and become a pagan, and adore the trees and the springs and the rocks and get power, as they call it! Nonsense!" ....

Two days later they found her body on the beach. As it was not proved that it was a case of suicide, Fray Bernardo had her buried in the graveyard. The next day Saturnino disappeared.......

We read in the diary: "I think my usefulness here is ended. Fray Bernardo agrees with me. I am going to write to Mexico and ask to be recalled. The Superiors will surely grant it. Fray Bernardo wants me to carry the letter myself, under the pretext of sending some urgent messages through me. The old Tallow is evidently anxious to get rid of me. Well, I don't care, I am too sick in my heart to resent the old pack-rat. . . ."

....

Fray Luis went out of the gate, leading his donkey, and mounted him outside. Thus he left the Mission, after embracing Fray Bernardo and receiving his blessing. The old man had said, ever fussy and anxious: "Now mind you take the road to the left, and stop tonight at Monterey, and tomorrow at the Soledad, and don't forget to leave that letter there, and then . . ."

"Yes, yes, yes, my dear Fray Bernardo, I remember all your instructions!" One more blessing, one more abrazo. . . . Fray Luis went through the gate and now he mounted his burro outside. His long legs were dangling. His head was bent over his breast, thinking and remembering, remembering way, way back, in Sevilla, in Malaga. . . . The burro ambled along by the sea, along the trail. Fray Luis dreamed and remembered, his long legs dangling. . . .

When he woke up and noticed, they were way down, way
down the south coast, where the River from the South opens into
the sea. And Fray Luis shrugged his shoulders and muttered:
"Why not this way? At any rate, I know this trail! Anda burro!"..

10
The Devil
is Paid in Full

They rode along the ridge, in the pale light of the very young moon. They rode along the ridge, the donkey and the monk. Along the ridge, along the ridge, in the pale light of the very young moon, southward, southward, to distant Mexico.

They came at last to the cross-trails, the trail to the rancheria, and the monk knew it.

"Hey! burro! where are you going, you idiot?" and he pulled on the reins.

The donkey kept on his way, down, to the left. Fray Luis pulled. He pulled and he tugged. He pulled frantically, but the donkey was on a run now, down, down, down the trail, dark,

dark, dark the trail under the trees.

"Hey! burro! Stop, you devil, stop, stop, stop!"

The branches were brushing his face in the darkness. He could hardly keep in the saddle. He grasped the reins. He grasped two antlers! He was riding a beetle, an immense, a gigantic beetle! He slid on its smooth black back from side to side. He grasped the antennae in utter terror. . . . Down, down, down the steep trail, the dark trail, down, down, down on the black back of the beetle. . . . They crossed the creek. The rancheria was dark and silent. The beetle scurried among the little conical huts. The beetle climbed to the roof of the ceremonial-house and Fray Luis hung desperately onto the loathesome antennae.

They stopped at the smoke-hole. The beetle looked down. Fray Luis, grasping the antennae, looked down.

There was a small fire burning inside, but there was nobody there except the old Blind Doctor. He was sitting against the north wall of the house.

The beetle scuttled back and Fray Luis slid over its head. He grasped the ends of the ladder. He descended the ladder. He brushed against a reata, nicely coiled, hanging from the center-pole. He went down the center-post ladder.

"Well! here I am, old man, here I am, here I am, here I am!" said Fray Luis. The old blind Amomuths never stirred.

And there they stood, a long time, for minutes, for a quarter of an hour, for almost an hour, looking at each other, the monk and the blind, the sightless old shaman, looking intently out of blind eyes. The fire crackled fitfully. They sat looking at each other.

It was a long, long time. Fray Luis grew restless. His mind wandered. Sevilla. Malaga. . . . Yaaaaah! He yelled in his terror. He opened his eyes, he looked, he yelled again, like a child. . . . The bear! the bear! where Amomuths had been sitting against the north wall . . . there was the bear, sitting against the north wall. . . . Fray Luis looked, utterly awake, at the bear sitting against the north wall of the ceremonial-house, and he yelled again. . . .

There they sat, facing each other, Amomuths and Fray Luis, Amomuths against the north wall and the monk with his back against the center-post.

Then it began again, the bear sitting there against the north wall, then Amomuths, then the bear. . . .

Fray Luis jumped up in terror. He could not keep his eyes from the bear-man, the horrible grizzly, immense, immobile against the north wall, sitting up. He felt back of him with his hand. He felt the ladder. Slowly, slowly, he went up, backwards, rung after rung, slowly, never dared he to turn his face.

And then he did. He turned his face. In a panic overwhelming, he turned. He turned around, he grasped the ladder, he ran up the ladder like a squirrel. . . . He could see the stars. . . . Their breath was in his face. . . .

Look out, Fray Luis, look out, slowly, take your time . . . slowly, look out for the reata. It is coiled neatly up there, in true vaquero style, with the loop ready . . . look out! Look out! Watch for your head. . . . My God! Don't put your head through the very loop!!! . . . Ah, there you have done it. Wait a minute! Don't struggle, don't struggle! It will choke you!!! Wait a . . .

Ah, there you have done it! ....

How your gaunt body swings at the end of the reata, Fray Luis! The shadows on the north wall swing, Fray Luis!

Peace be to your soul, Fray Luis.

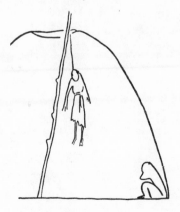

Coyote's Bones

When the late L.F. (Nancy) de Angulo, Eileen Callahan and I were first sifting through the de Angulo papers we came upon two full manuscripts of poems. The first contained mostly versions of Indian songs, and most of those had been inserted as a last minute chapter in *Indian Tales*. The second manuscript, however, seemed much more like fresh work, and must have been composed, we concluded, during de Angulo's last year in the Berkeley Hills. With the exception of the first half dozen or so poems, the poems which are presented here are drawn from that later manuscript.

Throughout his life Jaime de Angulo was always most at home among the poets. As early as 1919 we find him posing for a photograph with

Robinson Jeffers down at Big Sur. In later years, as we have mentioned, Ezra Pound became a great champion of his work. Mariane Moore was an irregular but always welcome correspondent; only a serious stroke prevented William Carlos Williams from writing the introduction to *Indian Tales*. "Out West" Kenneth Rexroth still remembers de Angulo fondly, and Robert Duncan became the regular family typist back in 1949. Indeed the list goes on. Phillip Lamantia remembers a wonderful afternoon in Big Sur listening attentively to de Angulo speaking on peyote; Jack Kerouac wrote about JDA in his book *Desolation Angels*. Allen Ginsberg, by way of Pound, hand-carried *Indian Tales* to his friend Carl Solomon, then editor at A.A. Wynn, and thus helped secure its eventual publication; and Gary Snyder introduced a whole new generation of readers to the accomplishments of Jaime de Angulo in his review of *Indian Tales* in *Earth Household*. Poets tend to know these things first, Old Coyote might have said.

Coyote's Bones

Coyote, ululating on the hill,
is it my fire that distresses you so?
Or the memories of long ago
when you were a man roaming the hills.

to-day
sixth of the month of the Rat
i visited the old palace

weeds grew in the courts
lizards ran along the walls
but in a silent inner hall i found a parchment
with figures and curves and equations
that i didnt understand

i took the parchment
hid it in my robes and stole away thru the courts
where the weeds grew
and the lizard ran along the walls
under the sky of dancing gold

In the desert
two snakes came out of my loins
the long one headed for the sunset
with the little one
viciously biting at his tail

in the foggy dawn of autumn
a faun was smiling in his beard
shuffling his cloven feet thru the dead leaves

Song of the Fire-wood

I am old, twisted, dry. I am cold.
Build the fire.
Heh! heeh-heh . . . he-he-he . . . feel good.
Let the chief call the dancers!

Old Kate's Medicine Song

Without a body I am
i am the song

Without a head I am
i am the head

i am a head without a song
i am rolling down the hill

Modoc War Song

I sat with my mother.
They made me a slave.

I sat with my mother
When they came.

I sing the songs of the Modok-ni.

fog coming up in streams
from the sea
In the pasture the old black mare stands
with her head bent.

Wildcat who stalks the trail alone
in broad daylight,
you are savage and proud.
No one will ever tame your heart.

beetle on the trail, have you seen my child?
I do not travel far, o man, ask the deer

deer, have you seen my child?
I live in the brush, o man, ask the condor in the sky

condor in the sky, have you seen my child?
I have not seen your child, but ask the cloud

cloud, have you seen my child?
the cloud drifted away on the wind

Indian fields over uplands
sky azure
and vultures flying,
mountains, mountains, abysses.

Indians singing together,
flute sad; the low flute,

and the horse walking, walking
strong under foreign saddle
and the bent rider. He shakes with fever;
and a girl riding pillion.

And the indians say:
"See that poor dago,
poor dago, high fever."

Holy shrine up aloft,
heap of stones, rather
where the indian porters pray to the Lake-Snake;
steady their loads with a head-band,
and every man adds a stone to the pile.

And the stranger gets down from his horse:
"I'm done, kid, get home without me."

The horse a good walker, good walker,
The indians inside their huts say:
"Look at that gal there, alone, going alone.
Dago's gal, with a face proud, proud,
That's what our chiefs were like in the old days."

And on the ridge under the blue air the vultures
with their elegant huge wings circling,
circling:
"Indian, dago, horse, jackass, cattle
all come to our table."

Soft days of autumn and silent space.
Tree, stalwart in the light of afternoon,
you fear neither the brooding solitude
nor the changing restless winds.

land of many hues
California of the climes
wide valleys parched in the sun

!   tsho, anda ganado, yeh, tsho   !

indios, and dead towns
where the coyotes howl
with the yellow moon

!   tsho, anda ganado, yeh, tsho   !

buckaroo from the north
take your turn at the rear
I lost my neckerchief in whoretown last night

sheepherder in the mountains
crazy with solitude
land of redwoods
land of spring flowers
sweet land of dead indians
land of ghosts

!   tsho, anda ganado, yeh, tsho   !

toll the mission bell
for the dead indian
for the friar in hell
conquistador, gambler,
whore and forty-niner

!   tsho, anda ganado, tsho   !

howl, coyote, howl to the yellow moon

dawn coming thru fog
ghostly trees
warm light in my study
birds in their cage waking up eating breakfast
i am reading about the birth of planets around the sun
gyrations of cosmic dust in ellipses

a spider is hanging her web from the sun-dial.
is she also wondering about time, infinity, and the stars?

grass and bamboo and eucalyptus in the rain
long white trunks swaying in the wind
a million sickle leaves gyrating
in a pulsating universe

but the bluejays are laughing
"gayo, gayo, run for home, philosopher!"

I doze on the beach
and remember the sullen sea, the joyous sea
the wine colored sea
and remember children screaming like gulls

They tell me about this and that
They tell me about their wives
And their husbands.
I look at the sea.

the animal-man dogs cats fishes
fill his rooms even a snake he sits
in the zoo the aquarium watching the ponderous
the slim but not the monkeys
on sunday when the jabber-crowd arrives
he goes back to his room

Dreaming, and dreaming, still dreaming
in the uncertain light of autumn,
a deer goes by in my garden . . .
i take my bow and slink after her.

I a seal lie on the rocks warm in the sun.

I remember the Esselen, the Mukne,
the Saklan, all the tribes that lived
From the Sur to San Francisco Bay.

I dive in the water, and my head looks like a man
Swimming to the shore in the dusk.

I like to wander along the bright streets
at night in the crowd.

Sun going down thru the Golden Gate
earlier and earlier every day
lighting this room where canaries
live with an old man

What are you planting, grandfather,
So carefully, in the spring:
Will it come, grandfather, with the crocus
And the lily?

It will come, my child, it will come
With the crocus and the lily,
With petals scarlet and anthers of gold,
It will come in the spring. Give me that hoe.

And what are you planting,
Grandfather in the spring?

My child, I am burying, give me that hoe,
I am planting, give me that hoe,

I am burying my heart,
Give me that hoe.

The Very Old Shaman

Useless
He sits in the sun
Where it has crept on him.

Hey! great-grand-son! Come here,
Please bring me a drink of water

Grandfather, the sky is clouding over,
it's going to rain, to storm!
let's run home!

        Slowly, grandchild, slowly.
Grandfather, let's take shelter
under yon redwood-tree.

        But the lightning might strike it.

Grandfather, grandfather! I'm scared!
the rain will drown us.

        Crawl into my shirt, grandchild;
        the sun will shine again.

Oh! Grandfather: the sun is out, the rain is over!
but the redwood-tree fell! Grandfather,
what are these things you were sitting on?

        Those are Coyote's bones, grandchild;
        the lightning never strikes over them.

Indians In Overalls

As indicated by dedicatory quote, *Indians in Overalls* invokes the spirit of Blaise Cendrars, a de Angulo favourite whom the author had met on an earlier visit to Europe. "In fact," Nancy de Angulo recalled, *"Indians in Overalls* started out as a letter to Cendrars, and then it just grew and grew."

It was, however, Ezra Pound who first championed this particular piece, and forwarded it to Fred Morgan to publish in an early issue of the *Hudson Review*. For some unknown reason de Angulo had begun to correspond with Pound upon the poet's incarceration (encagement?) at St. Elizabeth's. Robert Duncan, who was drawn to meet de Angulo by the advice of Pound, became the family typist at about this time, and remembers the correspondence as the work of "two brilliant old cranks, the one living in a cage, the other dying of cancer, contemplating the irony, and the absurdity, and the humour in their respective fates." Clearly it was Pound's efforts on de Angulo's behalf which brought to the author the brief period of national recognition he enjoyed just prior to his death in 1950, just a few months after this piece was first published.

C'est pour vous, Blaise Cendrars, que j'ai écrit ces lignes, parce que je savais que vous comprendriez. Vous qui avez vu tant de choses, tant de pays, tant de monde, vous qui aussi avez connu les indiens, vous qui n'avez peur ni de dieu ni du diable, ni de la vie ni de la mort.

Il n'y a rien, dans l'univers, de merveilleux. Il n'y a rien de caché. Le monde est un grand livre ouvert . . . mais il faut savoir lire, n'est-ce pas? C'est seulement la sottise humaine qui donne naissance au miracle (. . . et meême du vol en arrière!!).

Ce qui relie deux réalités, ce lien entre l'esprit et la matière, ce rapport entre ces deux choses . . . ah! C'est là le grand mystère! . . . comme l'a dit Lao-Sze il y a bien longtemps.

Indians In Overalls

A street in a little town on the high desert plateau of northeastern California. Clear air, blue sky, smell of sagebrush, smell of burning juniper wood. I was looking for Jack Folsom, an Indian of the Pit River tribe.

I saw some Paiutes loafing on a corner. I crossed over and asked them if Jack Folsom was in town. They did not answer me.

I strolled along with my hands in my pockets. Then I saw him, standing in front of a store. Same old Jack; squat, broad figure; very dark skin, gray hair; battered hat and brand-new overalls; and the same humorous, quizzical, gray eyes.

"Hallo, Jack."

"Why . . . Doc! Where you been all this time? What you doing here now? Looking for another cattle ranch?"

"No. No more cattle ranches for me. I came back here to study the Indian language."

"What you mean, Doc? You mean you want to learn our talk, Pit River talk? You can't do that, Doc, no use you trying. No white man can learn our words. There ain't a white man in this whole country can talk Pit River. Some fellows, some cowboys think they do, but all they know is a couple dirty words. Now, Modoc, or Paiute, that's easy talk. Why don't you try them? There is quite a few white men around here speak pretty good Paiute. I can talk Paiute, too. But Pit River, that's hard talk, Doc."

"Well, I can try, anyhow. Will you teach me?"

"Sure I will. Where you staying at, Doc?"

"Nowhere. I just got in on the train last night. Where are you living now, Jack?"

"Same old place. That little piece Indian land I got from the Government. I got a shack on it. Good water, I got a well. You been there before, Doc, you remember."

"Oh yes, I remember. Have you still got the same woman?"

"Yes, Lena. Big and fat. She still talks about you. She never knew a white man who was willing to sit down and eat with Indians!"

"Say, Jack, may I stay with you?"

"What you mean, Doc? You can't live with Indians!"

"Why not?"

"What would the white men say? They wouldn't allow you. They wouldn't talk to you. They would think you were a dog like us."

"To hell with the white men. I don't like them either. Will you let me stay with you?"

"Why sure I will! I have known you a long time, Doc. But I ain't got blankets enough . . . unless you want to get in bed with Lena and me, but that woman is too big. Ain't hardly room for me alone."

"That's all right, Jack. I'll go and buy some blankets."

"All right, Doc. Throw them in my wagon. That's my wagon there. I'll go and buy some grub. . . ."

All afternoon we drove through the sagebrush. Strong and pungent smell. Jackrabbits. Sometimes a clump of juniper trees, rough bark, gnarled branches. Wide, wide valley almost like a sea. Barely notice the mountains. Canyons with perpendicular sides and rim-rocks frowning. Jog, jog, jogging team of horses, a bay and a roan, raising the dust. There jumps another jackrabbit. Afternoon changing into sunset. A turn of the road around a hill. A crazy fence. Open the gate and almost fall with it. "Indian gate!" laughs Jack. Another turn around the hill in the gathering dusk, and there is the shack. Big fat Lena comes to the door. She sees me. She smiles: "Hallo, Doc!" just as if she had known I was coming, just as if I had left only last week. That was Lena. Always took life like that, as it came.

I had bought a tent and I put it up in the moonlight. It was September and already there was a chill to the night. Jack brought a rabbit-skin blanket and spread it on my bed. "Bet you'll need it before morning, Doc. You don't see many of these any more. Indians too lazy now. Takes hundred and fifty, maybe two hundred rabbits. Well, good night."

I scooped a hollow in the ground for my hips and got in under the blankets. I smoked a cigarette and listened to the coyotes howling and yapping out there in the moonlight. After a while the pack moved away into the distance and their bark was very faintly heard. Silence and moonlight through the tent door. I could not sleep. I smoked cigarette after cigarette. . . .

There was not much in that shack, except a few blankets on a pile of tule stalks in a corner. A good deal of the sky could be seen through the roof. There was a cooking stove, but it had no legs and reposed directly on the floor. Lena had removed the legs so that she could squat on the ground while cooking. She felt that was the proper way to cook, just like a campfire. Many Indian women are quite fat, but Lena was a very mountain of flesh, and getting to her feet was a strenuous operation. It surprised me to see how much she could do without raising her fundament from the floor. She could roll over and reach a frying pan six feet away. But "rolling over" does not describe adequately that peculiar motion, besides imparting to it something of the undignified. Have you ever observed in an aquarium an octopus creeping over a rock? It was a little like that. The rolls of flesh seemed to creep over the floor in advancing waves of cotton print, a brown arm uncoiled itself, the frying pan was reached inexorably.

Lena was not always cooking, although she always squatted on the floor. She also did beadwork, string beads of different colors in Indian designs, for belts, for hatbands, for tobacco pouches. The mind of a weaver must be a strange sort of mind, building a picture level after level. From side to side, from left to right, from right to left, it rises all along the line bit by bit. The whole composition has been visualized from the first and no retouching is possible. I used to wonder what went on in her head when her fat fingers got tired and she sat looking through the open door at the hills beyond. In the afternoons the sun came through the door, an autumn sun already, and the air was clear and bright. Lena spoke very little, and when she did it was in a very low voice, almost a whisper.

Big, placid, silent Lena, and her occasional chuckle. She and Jack got along very well. She was his fourth wife.

I said: "Jack, a while ago you called to me in English. You said 'let's eat.' Now, how would you say that in Indian?"

"*Laham.*"

I wrote it down in my notebook. Then I asked: "Which part in it means 'eat'?"

Jack looked at me with a very puzzled expression on his face. "I dunno what you mean, Doc, what part you eat. . . ."

"All right. . . . Never Mind. . . . How do you say 'I eat'?"

"*Saama.*"

"And how do you say 'You eat'?"

"Kaama."

"And how do you say 'He eats'?"

"Yaama."

I thought to myself: Of course! That's what the grammarians call pronominal prefixes. The *s . . . , k . . . ,* and *y . . . ,* stand for the pronouns, I, you, he. I felt very proud of myself. I was getting along fine. "And now, Jack, how do you say 'We eat'?"

"How many of us eat, Doc?"

"What's that got to do with it? If I say 'we,' I mean more than one. That's what we call singular and plural."

"I dunno what you call 'em things. I never went to school. But in Pit River talk it makes a lot of difference whether it's one man, or two people, or more than two people. For instance, you and me sit here, and here comes another fellow, and he says: 'You fellows eat already?' Well, we answer in Indian: *Sahaama*. That means: 'Yes, we two eat already.' But if we had been more than two, like for instance you and me and Lena, then we would say: *Sahammiima*. 'Yes, we all eat already.' Just like you say to a fellow if you invite him to eat: *Tamma*. That means: 'You, eat!' But if you are talking to two people you say: *Dzammi*. And if it's more than two you say: *Dzamma*. Savvy now, Doc?"

I was jubilant. "Why yes, Jack. It's what they call the dual. That's the way it is in Greek!" Jack had a very kind face, and it was now wreathed in smiles. He evidently felt very proud of the Greeks. He said: "Well, well. What do you think of that now! I always thought them Greeks were nice people."

I was astounded. "What do you know about the Greeks, Jack?"

"They was a couple of them had a restaurant here a while back. I used to listen to their talk but I couldn't get a word of it, although I know some Mexican too. I didn't know they talk like us."

Jack got up from the log where we had been sitting. "Let's go and hunt some rabbits, Doc." He went into the shack and came

out again with his shotgun, and we wandered out into the tall
sagebrush. "When I was a little boy I used to hunt them with bow
and arrow. That's a long time ago, when I was a little boy. . . ."
"How old are you, Jack?" "I dunno, Doc. Old-time Indians don't
know their age. I'll tell you though, and mebbe you can figure it
out. I remember I was a young man able to ride a horse at the time
of the Modoc War. I was one of the first boys had the nerve to ride
a horse. The old people were still afraid of them. That's why old
man Folsom kind of adopted me. He was a white man. Him and
his wife didn't have any children, and so they raised me like their
own child. They were about the first white people to settle around
here. When they died and I went back to my own people, I felt
like a stranger for a long time."

"Say, Doc, I want you to write a letter for me. It's to Jack
Spring. You remember him, at Hot Spring, what we call Astaghiwa. . . . Well, tell him I got his colt ready. Tell him come and
get him and don't let any them young Indians make him buck for
fun because he'll be a spoilt horse before you know. . . . And tell
him a Paiute boy shot old Blind Hall, you know, the old Indian
doctor, over at Big Meadows last week on account old Hall
poisoned his relations. He fired six shots point-blank but it didn't
hurt him at all because he was not there. Old Hall laughed like
hell about it. Said his medicine, Raven, warned him that Paiute
boy was coming, so he went away and left his shadow there and
the Paiute emptied his gun at it. . . . And tell him if he has got a
rawhide to save it for me because I got an order for hackamores
and quirts, and I am short of strings, and I'll pay him for it. . . .
And tell him that old Bob Chief at Tulukupi is pretty sick and
maybe he going to die and we know who poisoned him, but we
got some doctors on our side too. . . . Well, that's all I guess, and
tell him to take care of himself."

I wandered around in the sagebrush. I was thinking about
this Pit River language. I could see already that it was going to be

a very difficult language to study, a very complex language, structurally complex. And yet the Pit River Indians were accounted one of the most primitive tribes among the California Indians, extremely primitive, just about at the level of the Stone Age in culture. And so I wondered . . . Could it be that there was no relation between language and culture?

"I was born in an old-time Indian house, Doc. There ain't any more that kind left, old-time Indian houses. Nowadays Indian people live in houses like the white people. But that's no good because their houses are not well built like the houses of the white men. Indians' houses is nothing but shacks full of drafts and holes in the roof. Why! some of them is just made out of tin cans, you must have seen them by the railroad track in town, what they call Indiantown. This is awful cold country in winter, snow, blizzard, wind blows through. Indians catch cold and die. And we didn't wear clothes in them days and so everybody was tough and healthy. But now the Indians can't stand the cold weather any better than a white man, and even worse. We are all going to die. . . .

"The old-time Indian house, that's what we call *astsuy*. Now, I bet you can't say that word right, Doc." I tried and Jack laughed. "No, you didn't say 'house,' you said 'winter.' Them two words is pretty much alike, ain't they, *astsuy* and *astsuy*. One means 'House' and the other means 'winter' but the white people never can tell the difference."

"Where does the difference come in, Jack?"

"I dunno, Doc, I couldn't tell you, but they sound different to me. Any Indian will tell you they are different: *astsuy, astsuy.*"

I repeated after him again and again, and he laughed and laughed. Finally I caught on: it was a question of tone, pitch-tone: *astsuy* and *astsuy*. There are two tones in Pit River, high tone and low tone. Every syllable of every word is in either high or low tone, the difference being about a musical fourth (as from *do* to *fa*). Of course the Indians themselves do not realize it any more than the average white man is aware of stress-accent in his own language. But it is an essential part of the Pit River grammar.

In the old days the Pit River Indians did not live in individual houses. In summertime they camped around in the hills and the valleys, here and there, moving about in small groups somewhat like our own families, fishing, hunting, gathering crops of roots and seeds, and practicing conscientiously a lot of good healthy loafing. In the fall, when the nights were getting sharp and the mule-deer were turning red, all these wandering small families returned home, converging from the hills, from the higher valleys and swales, down the canyons, through the juniper, through the forests of tall pine, down to the sagebrush flats, all trekking home to some wintering ground, at Astaghiwa where there is a spring of hot water, at Tapaslu where the valley ends in a cul-de-sac, at Dalmo'ma where there are lots of wild turnips, to all the wintering grounds, there to dig themselves in for the coming winter and snow and blizzards and days of calm with the sun shining bright and the air cracking with frost.

You can imagine them, straggling home, the men usually stark naked, or some with a loin-cloth or a G-string; the women wore a kind of apron or hulaskirt of reeds; they carried their burdens on their backs from tump-lines from the forehead or from above the breast, both men and women, for there was not much division of labor among these Indians, except that the men did all the hunting with bow and arrows; they all wore their hair long and often coiled it in a chignon and stuck a long wooden pin to hold it in place. There they come down the trail in single file, grunting under their packs, squat bodies with broad shoulders, skins of chocolate—although many are tall and lithe, like the Paiutes of the Nevada desert with whom they intermarried much. There are not many children because only the most sturdy and the most lucky can survive.

And now, from everywhere around they arrive at the winter grounds, one family today, another the next, and another, and another. Here's old Red Tracks and his people: that young woman there, she is related to me, and who is that young fellow, seems to me I have seem him somewhere. I don't think he is a relation of mine, oh! and look at the woman of Stalks-in-the-reeds, she is packing a new baby. . . . *"Is kaadzi! Is kaakaadzi!* Man, you are living! Man, you are living! We got here five days ago. . . . Where is Standing-alone?" "Oh, he left us, said he was going to winter at Hanti'u, he has relations there. Has the old Blind Chief arrived?" "No, but there are four, five chiefs here already. . . ."

There would be forty, fifty, sixty people, wintering at one place, all of them living together, living on top of each other, in one big communal house, a kind of underground cave. That was the *astsuy,* no, I mean the *astsuy.*

I should have given a great deal to have been able to spend some time in one of those old-time winter houses, and see just exactly how did life go on, get a real feeling of their social organization, their family life, their kinship system. All these are just words. I had read them in books on anthropology, but they were just labels, dried specimens, lifeless.

I had always wanted to live with really primitive people, real Stone Age men, and see how they thought, and felt. I had read books on primitive psychology, some of them excellent books like Lévy Brühl's (who, by the way, never left Paris, or so I have been told), but I wasn't convinced. All that was too theoretical.

Really primitive people, not like the already cultured Indians of the Southwest with their sun-worship, their secret societies, their esoteric ceremonials. But real Stone Age men. . . . Well, these had been it, until a very short time ago. Here was Jack Folsom who was a little boy when the first white men arrived. Was there anything left? How much had they changed? My God, think of it, to pass in one lifetime from the stone axe to wireless telegraphy! Indians in overalls; no, there was nothing picturesque about these Indians, no feather headdresses or beaded moccasins, nothing to delight the tourists about these "digger Indians" in their battered hats and cheap calicos, picking the offal of the whites on the garbage dumps at the edge of town. My Indians in overalls! . . .

Jack said he had to go away for a while, had to go after a

horse of his. He owned several good fast horses, which he raced sometimes, and made a little money that way. (The Indians had to live somehow or other—they had received a few pieces of land, here and there, from the Government, mostly rocky spots without water, useless—in the summer's haying time they could make a few bucks working for the white ranchers—the rest of the time, who in the hell cared: The sons-of-bitches were no good, liars and thieves, let them all die.) He said he would be back in a week or two. So, after he left with Lena and the spring-wagon, I saddled the remaining horse, tied my blankets behind the saddle, and went off for a jaunt.

I followed the Pit River downstream, stopped at Canby to buy a can of beans and some bacon at the store (Canby at that time consisted of one store, one blacksmith shop, and three other houses). The fellow there recognized me. "Say, ain't you Buckaroo Doc? Well, I'll be darned! Where've you been? Remember that time you rode to the show and you didn't have no pants on, nothing but a machinaw and your chaps and spurs, and you walked onto the stage with a bottle of whiskey by mistake, and for a while everybody thought you were one of the actors? We still laugh about it around here. What are you doing now? I thought you had left and gone to the lower country . . ." etc., etc.

I went on down, and camped that night in a clump of junipers. Next day I came out of the hills into the Big Valley (*wa'wa atwam* of the Indians). I passed a little bit of a town called Bieber. Again I bought some grub at the store. The people there seemed to be half-witted and I had a hard time to make myself understood. All the whites in that part of the country are slow, uncouth pioneers. At least they were, at that time.

I went on. It was getting dark and I was looking for a place to camp. Then, not far from the road, I saw a fire burning and some people camping under a big tall pine. I went over, and that's how I made the acquaintance of Sukmit, alias Frank Martin, also known as Bieber Frank, also as "that crazy hunchback Indian doctor," who later became my inseparable companion—(how many ditches have we shared for a bed with a bottle of fire-water?!). Crazy as they come, long powerful arms, one eye gone, the other malicious, an enormous leering mouth with a few teeth here and there. He was a young man in his thirties.

"Hallo, can I camp here?"

"Sure! Why not? This is my land, Indian land, I am not like white man, I let everybody stay on me. Everybody welcome, I am Indian doctor. Where you come from? Where you going? Sit down here with us. I bet you never eat acorn-mush before. Taste better with salt. Old-time Indians didn't have salt. You eat salt and it give you sore eyes."

He turned to an old fat woman and started to talk fast in Pit River. They spoke much more clearly than Jack Folsom. Again I noticed the same curious singsong of high and low tones, of long and short syllables, like a Morse code. And what harsh gutturals! These two seemed to be always shouting at the top of their voices, like Spaniards (in fact, most Pit Rivers do). There was also another Indian woman sitting by the fire. She was little and scrawny, and she didn't say anything. Sukmit pointed to her and said: "He is my uncle. He don't speak white language. I ain't got hay for your horse. Will he stand staking?"

The acorn-mush tasted like pea-soup, more or less. There were also fried potatoes, but I had never eaten potatoes fried just like that, sort of parboiled in grease in a slow skillet. I found them revolting but ate them to be polite. Sukmit kept on talking and boasting. Once in a while, his mother, the fat woman, would stop poking the fire, look at him and say in English: "Oh, you are crazy." "She says I am crazy because I am a doctor, all Indian doctors are crazy." The other woman, the "uncle," did not say anything. She never did. She died two years later.

The old lady, however, I mean Sukmit's mother, was very active. Active, that is, with her mouth. Her backside never moved from the ground. From there she carried on a never-ending battle with her son. She stirred the mush while he went on ranting about his powers as a medicine-man, and every once in a while she would ejaculate the "Oh, you are crazy!" and there would be a short skirmish in shouted Pit River. She had a broad face, dark chocolate, and her eyes had already the thin veil of cataract. She was always gay and laughed a good deal.

Another woman appeared in the firelight. They said her name was Kate Gordon and she had married three husbands, all of them white men. "I like white men," she said, "they treat me fine. Give me plenty grub, lots clothes. . . . You want to marry me, white man?" I said no, I was already married. She was a handsome old girl, with gray hair and fiery eyes. She was evidently manic. (I have found that type, the manic, quite frequently among the Pit Rivers.)

There was something very friendly and warm about Sukmit, in spite of his shouting and boasting, something childlike. I had always thought of medicine-men as old and crafty. As I have said, Sukmit was in his thirties. He had a very keen sense of humor and was forever joking. But one felt a strange sadness, a wistfulness, underneath it all, and ofttimes he dropped into a reverie and went on with his work (for he was very active—always doing something, sawing wood, repairing his car, this, that) like an automaton.

I have seen other Indians, and many white men too, who often drop into this trancelike automatism. Fantasy is an active occupation of the mind which demands concentration, a narrowing of the consciousness to a focus. Some people can do it sitting down with their chin in their hand, but not your extrovert with his too much thyroid; hence that automaton-like activity—but the mind is a million miles away. Sukmit had a drag-saw for cutting logs, operated by a small engine and a dry battery (at least he said it was; I don't know much about machinery and care less; like Sukmit's mother I was born before the days of the machine). The old lady felt a great admiration for her son, and a little distrust. I shared both attitudes.

Sukmit was a better informant than Jack, linguistically. By this time I had discovered that there were six modes in the Pit

River verb: indicative, subjunctive, interrogative, volitional present or future, and optative (Oh, those so-simple languages of the primitive peoples!); but it was impossible to make Jack stick to one mode. In giving me a paradigm (I eat, you eat, he eats . . . etc.), he would jump from one mode to another. Not so with Sukmit; once started on one mode he followed it rigidly. The old lady was a different type again; she wasn't going to follow any paradigms. She changed from one verb to another if she thought it was more interesting—on the other hand, she was excellent at dissecting a long periphrastic form into its component parts. I would exclaim "Oh . . . I see . . ." and she would chuckle: "Ha . . . ha . . . ha . . . you white man!" When she chuckled, her belly also chuckled.

Sukmit and his mother were forever quarreling, usually in Pit River, but sometimes in English for my edification. At first it worried me, but after a while I paid no more attention to it than to the breeze. The old lady had been born in an old-time Indian house. She described it to me in detail, and even made me a little model of it one day with sticks and bits of mud. She was very keen at explaining to me many apparently meaningless details, which become quite important when you consider the realities of life, and the necessities of a materially primitive culture. She had been born and reared in such a culture and had an artist's eye for the significant differences. For instance, she was explaining to me that there was no door in the communal winter house (which was really a sort of cave or cellar dug out of the ground and roofed over with sod)—people went in or out through the smoke-hole by climbing a stepladder set up against the center-post. But at one end of the house there was a tunnel that led out to the outside ground, like a rabbit warren. This was for purposes of ventilation, of establishing a draft of air into and through the crowded house and out through the smoke-hole. The chiefs, the important men, usually sat or lay there on their backs, smoking their stonepipes and enjoying the fresh air (forty or fifty humans including babies can make a thick atmosphere!). Now, mothers and fathers climbed the ladder with small children in their arms, or on the hip, or strapped to the cradle-board; but bigger youngsters crawled out through the rabbit warren; and the chiefs would grab them, and hug them, and tease them, as grownups do the world over. Such a description put the whole picture in focus for me. And again the old lady (who had a pornographic mind) would say: ". . . the smoke-hole pretty big—have to step across, grab pole—young girl take time step across show everything. . . . Ha, ha, ha! . . . you white man, ha, ha, ha! . . ."

The old lady Gordon, she of the gray hair and fiery eyes, was a very different type. As we were sitting by the campfire she told me of the wars they had with the Paiutes and the Modocs. It seems that the Indians like to meet in two enemy lines facing each other and shoot with bow and arrow. Each woman stood behind her man, holding onto his belt, and passed the arrows to his hand. After the fight they danced to placate the shadows of the dead. They strung the ears on an arrow shaft and held them to the fire and chanted. Old Gordon took a stick and held it to the fire and chanted in a deep contralto. It was weird and made me shiver. For once, Sukmit was silent, but old Mary had to break the silence and chuckle: ". . . Ha, ha, ha . . . you white man . . ."

I only stayed a few days with Sukmit and his people, that time. One morning he started to move camp, piling things into his decrepit automobile, and I saddled my horse. But his departure was in the grand manner. I must explain that Indians' cars, in those days, were of the "tin lizzie" type, held together with bale-wire. This was before the days of the self-starter—and cranking the engine was a back-breaking and discouraging task. Indians had discovered a very good way to start the engine: prop up the hind end of the car with a jack, then start the engine by spinning the rear wheels, then kick off the jack, run after the car as it zig-zagged through the sagebrush, climb in at the back, and grab the steering wheel. Very good, but hard for Sukmit the hunchback. That morning, there was a heated discussion between him and the old lady. He wanted her to sit at the wheel and steer the car while he started it Indian fashion. But she would have none of it. He argued and argued that it was easy, very easy. But she was obdurate. Finally he yelled: "Get in, Christ Almighty, do you want to live forever?"

I started back along the Pit River toward the Hot Springs. I saw a dilapidated shack and went in. There was an Indian girl in there. She was tattooing her wrist with an indelible pencil and a sewing needle. She sat in a chair by the window, pricking, pricking. She was tattooing two initials on her left wrist: B. H. Her face was fat, commonplace, and unreadable. She wore a yellow dress and her legs popped out of tight-laced high-heeled shoes. She sat by the window, pricking and mixing blood and indelible pencil into B. H. She was through with the B and was starting on the H. Through the window one saw the flats of sage-brush and gnarled juniper trees, and in the distance Wadaqtsuudzi, the big mountain where there is a lake on top, and men go there who are seeking power. As I went out of the room, I noticed an iron bedstead. It was held together by a pair of pink corsets laced from one post to the other. On a dressing-table a box of Jonteel face powder. I was thinking of that old woman who gave me wild turnips to eat at Sukmit's camp, she of the gray hair and burning eyes, who sang the chant for appeasing the dead enemies. She had the traditional tattoo lines on the chin. How she cursed the Modocs! They had killed her father and taken her mother captive. She also taught me a war-song, a monotonous kind of wail. She said her mother used to sing it when they were alone, and she would cry.

I had gone into that house looking for an old fellow named Blind Hall, or Johnny Hall (his name, I found out later, was Tahteumi, meaning "red trail," or "red track," or "sunset trail"). They had told me he was one of the most powerful medicine-men around. But the tattooing girl said he wasn't there; this was his house, but he had gone to another camp. She said he was sick. "He was going to town the other day with his old woman: they

were driving along in their old buggy; automobile come from behind; upset buggy; old Hall didn't know he was hurt, but he must
have dropped his shadow; he went on to Hantiyu, but he got
pretty sick; he is coming back today; he is going to doctor himself
tonight."

That sounded interesting. I thought I would hang around.
Maybe I would learn something. So I wandered around. About
noon Blind Hall arrived in the old rattling creaking swaying
buggy with his old woman and the old old decrepit horse. I knew
right away I had seen him before somewhere, sometime; that
massive face, the sightless eyes, the very thick lips and quite a lot
of white beard for an Indian. "Hallo, white man, I remember you,
you stop once, we camp side road, you give me can beans, bacon,
you eat with us, you treat me good, you all right, I remember you,
I remember your voice—I am pretty sick now, dropped my
shadow on the road, can't live without my shadow, maybe I die, I
dunno. . . . I doctor myself tonight. You stay, you help sing tonight."

Blind Hall called his medicine "my poison." The Indian word
is *damaagome*. Some Indians translate it in English as "medicine,"
or "power," sometimes "dog" (in the sense of pet dog, or trained
dog). Blind Hall was not boastful like Sukmit; he was full of quiet
dignity; as to his age, goodness knows, he said he and Jack Folsom were young men together, and once they got mad at each
other: "I called him by his name and he called my by my name"
(you are not supposed to call an Indian by his personal name;
that's too personal, too private; you call him by his term of relationship to you—uncle, grandfather, brother-in-law, or whatever—or by his nickname).

Blind Hall was groaning and bellyaching about the pain in
his ribs. We were sitting in the sun. "Give me a cigarette, white
man. Mebbe I die. I dunno. That autocar he knock my shadow
out of me; shadow he stay on the road, now can't find me; can't
live without my shadow! . . . It's too bad, mebbe I die . . . tonight

I doctor myself, I ask my poisons . . . I got several poisons . . . I got Raven, he live on top mountain Wadaqtsuudzi, he know everything, watch everything. . . . I got Bullsnake, he pretty good too. . . . I got Louse, Crablouse, live with people, much friends, he tell me lots things. . . . I got Jim Lizard, he sit on rock all day, he pretty clever but not serious, he damn liar. . . . Sometime I doctor sick man, call my poisons come over my head, they fight, Raven says that man poisoned, Bullsnake say no he not poisoned, he broke rule hunting . . . and then this here Jim Lizard he say, Oh! let's go home that man going to die anyhow! . . . Then Raven he shake his finger at him he say: Who ask you what you think? Why don't you help our father?" (The poisons call the medicine-man "my father," *ittu ai*—the medicine-man calls his poison *ittu damaagome* "my *damaagome*," or whatever you want to translate that word by: medicine, poison, power. . . .) "You can go home if you want to, we will stay here and help our father. Then Jim Lizard mebbe he stay and help and mebbe he tell me lie. I can't depend on him. . . . Ohh . . . it hurt me inside here. Maybe I die. Everybody die sometime. . . . I ask my poison tonight. You white man, you help, you sing too. More people sing more good. Sometime my poison very far away, not hear. Lots people sing, he hear better."

At this place of Astaghiwa (meaning "hot being," because there is a hot spring) there also lived Robert Spring (he took the name from the spring—but his brother was Jim Bailey, and why?? but Jim Bailey was the son of Blind Hall's woman, but Blind Hall was not his father. . . . Indian relationships are very complex, and the adoption of white men's names does not simplify things.) This Robert Spring was a very quiet individual, very shy, about thirty-five years old, well set up, spoke English fairly well. He asked me to show him how he could write his own language: "I been to school at Fort Bidwell; I can write English; I try to write our language but can't do it. Yet you do it. Will you show me?" It was interesting to see that he was aware of the differences due to tones, but of course he had no idea of arranging tones in a sequence or scale. And *my* conception of a tone as "low" and another as "high" was extremely puzzling to him. "Why don't you say that one is to the right and the other to the left?" he asked. I had no answer, of course.

We were sitting on a log. He said: "Goddammit! an Indian camp is always dirty. . . . Look at that!" In truth it was pretty messy: broken wagon-wheels askew against a juniper trunk. A couple of shacks made of boards and flattened tin cans for roof. A tent. Piles of ashes, old campfires. Tin cans, tin cans, tin cans. A broken coffee pot—but a beautiful panoramic view. Undulations of sagebrush and the distant mountains all around. This is a country of vast distances. That does not look like such a big hill over there . . . but it rises three thousand feet and it is about fifteen miles from here. Very fooling, this clear atmosphere.

A buggy rattled in. There were two old Indians in it, a man and a woman. "That's Hantiyu Bill. You wouldn't think so but that fellow is pretty old. He got that woman as a present. They used to do that in the old days sometimes. Her father and Bill were great friends and he gave the woman to him."

I asked him about that "shadow" that Blind Hall had lost. "That's what we call the *de'lamdzi*," he said. "Does that mean 'shadow,' like the shadow of a tree? Or does it mean shadow like what the white people call the 'soul'?" "I dunno about that last word, how you pronounce it? I have heard the white people talk about it but I don't understand what it means. But the shadow from a tree, that's different. That's *dalilamdzi*. Yes, they sound very much the same, don't they? I never noticed that before, *de'lamdzi, dalilamdzi. . . .*"[1]

---

[1] I found out later that *de'lamdzi* is a noun, while *dalilamdzi* is a verb. Thus:

    salilamdzi—I make a shadow (on the ground)

    ittu dalilamdzi—my shadow (on the ground)

    ittu de'lamdzi—my shadow (in the sense of soul)

Compare Latin *"anima,"* a current of air, wind, breath, vital principle. The etymology of Anglo-Saxon "soul" is unknown.

His mother, old Hall's woman, passes by. She is going to dig for roots, on the flats. Little old woman, all wrinkles, bent over under her conical pack-basket, tottering away with the help of her digging stick. She is eternally mumbling something. Once in a while she pokes into the ground, bends over, pulls a wild turnip and throws it over her shoulder into the pack-basket on her back. She looks very small in all that vastness of landscape. Robert Spring watches her and smiles: "See, she thinks she is helping. Old people are like that."

Robert Spring had a good ear; he would have been an excellent phonetician. He made me notice the difference between *dihoomi* "to run," and *dihommi* "the wind." A question of length: in one the vowel is long; in the other it is the consonant which is long. Quantity is as important in this language as it is in Latin prosody.

That evening we all gathered at sundown. Jack Steel, an Indian from Han ho ally acted as Blind Hall's "interpreter," had arrived. He went out a little way into the sagebrush and called the poisons. "Raven, you, my poison, COME! (*qaq, mi', ittu damaagome, tunnoo*). . . . Bull-snake, my poison, come. . . . Crablouse, my poison, cooome. . . . You all, my poisons, COOOME!!" It was kind of weird, this man out in the sagebrush calling and calling for the poisons, just like a farmer calling his cows home.

We all gathered around the fire; some were sitting on the ground, some were lying on their side. Blind Hall began singing one of his medicine-songs. Two or three who knew that song well joined him. Others hummed for a while before catching on. Robert Spring said to me: "Come on, sing. Don't be afraid. Everybody must help." At that time I had not yet learned to sing Indian fashion. The melody puzzled me. But I joined in, bashfully at first, then when I realized that nobody was paying any attention to me, with gusto.

Blind Hall had soon stopped singing, himself. He had dropped into a sort of brown study, or as if he were listening to something inside his belly. Suddenly he clapped his hands, the

singing stopped abruptly. In the silence he shouted something
which the "interpreter," Jack Steel, repeated. And before Jack
Steel was through, Blind Hall was shouting again, which the interpreter also repeated, and so on, five or six times. It was not an
exchange between Blind Hall and Jack Steel. Jack Steel was simply
repeating word for word what Blind Hall was shouting. It was
an exchange between Hall and his poison, Raven. First, Hall
would shout a query which the interpreter repeated; then Hall
would listen to what Raven (hovering unseen above our heads)
was answering—and he would repeat that answer of Raven which
he, Hall, had heard in his mind—and the interpreter would repeat
the repetition. Then Hall emitted a sort of grunted "Aaaah. . . ,"
and relapsed into a brown study. Everybody else, Jack Steel included, relaxed. Some lit cigarettes; others gossiped. A woman
said to me: "You did pretty good; you help; that's good!" Robert
Spring said: "Sure, everybody must help. Sometimes the poisons
are far away. They don't hear. Everybody must sing together
to wake them up."

The woman who had praised me for singing said for my
benefit: "He ask his Raven if he going to die. Raven say he don't
know; ask the others." Blind Hall started humming another
medicine-song, and everything went on like before. That way
four or five times. At one time he got pretty excited and started to
jump and dance, and fell down. It must be hell to be blind.

The whole performance lasted about a couple of hours. Then
everybody dispersed.

The next morning Blind Hall felt much better. I asked
Robert Spring about the "interpreter." They call it *astumage,*
which literally means translating or interpreting. According to
Spring, the medicine-man gets so excited that his speech often becomes quite unintelligible; but his interpreter is used to it and
able to repeat it clearly. Quite so; he evidently performs that
function. But I suspect something else, not so visible: the shaman
is in a great state of excitement, it borders on hysteria, even
catalepsy sometimes; it seems to me that it would be pretty easy

Old Blind Hall and Jaime de Angulo

for the shaman to slip into the autistic stage of schizophrenia . . .
and never come back to reality! Is it not possible, perhaps, that the
interpreter acts as a link, a life-line by which the shaman remains
in contact with the reality of the material world?

Blind Hall was so pleased with my "helping" that he offered
to make me some moccasins if I got him a piece of buckskin. Poor
old blind fellow! *Some* moccasins!! They might have fitted the foot
of a dinosaur, or some such beast, but not a human foot. However I assured him they fitted my feet like gloves and he was very
proud.

It was Robert Spring who first made me understand about
the *dinihowi*. "That's what we Indians call *luck*. A man has got to
have luck, no matter for what, whether it's for gambling, or for
hunting, for making love, for anything, unless he wants to be just
a common Indian . . . like me."

We were lying flat on our backs under a juniper. After a silence he started again: "When a fellow is young, everybody is
after him to go to the mountains and get himself a *dinihowi*. The
old men say: "You'll never amount to anything if you don't go
and catch a *dinihowi*. And then you hear other fellows brag about
their luck at gambling, or how they got a good *dinihowi* for
hunting. Well, there come a time when a young fellow starts to
feel uneasy, kind of sad, kind of worried, that's just about the time
he's getting to be a man grown up. Then he start to 'wander,'
that's what we call it, wandering. They say: Leave him alone, he is
wandering. That's the time you go to the hills, you don't come
home, you stay out all night, you get scared, you cry; two, three
days you go hungry. Sometime your people get worried, come
after you, but you throw rocks at them: Go away, I don't want
you, leave me alone. You get pretty hungry, you get dizzy, you are
afraid of grizzly bears. Maybe you fall asleep and someone come
wake you up, maybe a wolf, push your head with his foot, maybe
bluejay peck at your face, maybe little fly get in your ear, he say:
Hey! Wake up! What you doing here? Your people worrying

about you! You better go home! I seen you wandering here, crying, hungry, I pity you, I like you. I help you. Listen, this is my
song. Remember that song. When you want me, you come here
and sing my song. I'll hear you. I'll come. . . ."

I said to Robert Spring: "But then, I don't see what is the
difference between the *dinihowi* and the *damaagome*. . . ." "There is
no difference. It's all the same. Only the *damaagome* that's for
doctors." "How does the doctor get his *damaagomes*?" "Just like
you and me get a *dinihowi*. He goes to the mountain. He cries.
Then someone comes and says, this is my song, I'll help you."
"Well, then, I don't see any difference." "I am telling you there is
no difference. Only the *dinihowi* that's for plain Indians like you
and me, and the *damaagome* that's for doctors. . . . Well, I'll tell
you, there is maybe some difference. The *damaagome* is kind of
mean, quarrelsome, always fighting. The *dinihowi* is more peace-
ful."

There came a figure lurching toward us with a curious gait,
something like an orangutan, through the sagebrush. Robert
Spring chuckled: "There comes your friend." Sure enough, it was
Sukmit. "How did you know he and I were friends?" "Oh, Indians hear everything. It don't take long for news to travel in the
sagebrush. I heard all about you stopping at his camp." Sukmit
greeted me: "Hallo, Jaime!" (He was the only Pit River who ever
called me by my first name. The others used my nickname in that
country, Buckaroo Doc, or just Doc.) Then he and Robert Spring
greeted each other: *Is, kaakaadzi* (Person, you are living). He sat
down on one knee, which was his usual posture. "I heard Doctor
Hall was sick, so I came to help," he said.

Now, that puzzled me. I had always heard that Indian shamans cordially detested each other. We told Sukmit that Hall had
doctored himself and was now feeling better. "That's good," he
said.

We all three went looking for the old man and found him sitting on a bench with his back to the shack and chewing tobacco.

Robert Spring sat himself next to him and Sukmit and I on the ground in front, but careful to leave a clear space for the old blind man to spit into. Then there ensued the, to me, most amazing conversation about doctors and their poisons. Blind Hall started again on his pet subject of complaint: his pet *damaagome*, Jim Lizard, the lying sonofabitch, he could never trust . . . but this time he had behaved himself, he wasn't mean enough to fool his own father when his father was sick, etc., etc. And Sukmit to corroborate: "Yes, some of them *damaagomes* is mean. When I started doctoring I tried a trick. I tried bringing my poison to a hand-game. Now, a doctor is not supposed to use his poison for gambling (this was addressed to me, not to Hall or Robert Spring). It's against the rules. But I thought I was smart, see. I thought to hell with the rules, I do like white man, see. Well, in the middle of the game I got awful thirsty, and I get up and go to the spring, and I take a long drink of water, and I got awful dizzy and sick, I got cramps, I puke. . . . See, my *damaagome* he do that, he mad because I bring him to hand-game, not supposed to do that." Blind Hall was roaring with laughter. "Ha, ha, ha. Your poison he make you sick. You bring him to hand-game, he make you sick. Ha, ha, ha."

Sukmit thought for a while, then he said: "Them *damaagomes* is dangerous things to handle. That's why I stick to my own and I don't try to steal other doctors' *damaagomes*. But this old man here, Doctor Hall, he don't care, he steal other doctors' *damaagomes!*" Blind Hall guffawed: "Sure I do! I steal other doctors' *damaagomes*. They steal mine, too, if they can. They try to steal my Raven, but he won't follow them. Ha, ha!" Sukmit said: "That's a good one, your Raven. I would like to have him myself. But I don't like to fool with other people's poisons. It may be a bad one and you can't handle him and he make you sick." Blind Hall laughed again: "I am not afraid of them!"

Later on that day I asked Robert Spring: "How do the doctors steal each other's *damaagomes*?" "I dunno, Doc, I am not a doctor. But you heard Blind Hall say so himself. How do you steal another man's dog?"

I stayed a few days longer at that camp, then I decided to go back to Alturas and see if Jack Folsom was back at his place. I went north by Hantiyu. Toward evening I made my camp in a swale where there was a brook. There was another camp a few hundred yards upstream from me. After eating I strolled over there. Indians, a middle-aged man, a young woman, and a child. The man was surly: "What you want?" "Nothing. I just came to visit." "I don't want no visit! That's your camp over there. Stay over there. You come my country. You kill my people. You take my land. This is my camp. Leave me alone."

As I went the woman gave me an apologetic smile: "He cross fellow. He don't like white people." Anyone could see that.

I found Jack Folsom and Lena at their place. He told me that the Pit Rivers have a word for "year" and one for "month." The word for month is the same as that for moon, of course. What surprised me was that they use the same word (*tsulh*) for sun and moon; if they want to specify, they say "night *tsulh*" or "day *tsulh*."[2] They named the months: month of the groundhog; month of the squirrel; month of the wild turnips; month of the deer running, etc. They had twelve such months, and every fourth year they repeated the midwinter month (they were aware of the solstices). This was the occasion for a lot of quarrelling. As Jack Folsom put it: "It used to get pretty stinky in the winter house, especially after Indians got dogs.[3] After two or three months of winter the litter of tules was lousy with vermin and fleas and bugs. People scratch all the time, want to get out go to the hills. Mebbe next moon is groundhog moon, and then next is squirrel moon, and then wild-turnip moon, that's the time people get out and go to the hills. They were in a hurry for the winter to end. And they

---

[2] In the myths of many California tribes the moon is a man and the sun a woman. Among the Pit Rivers, however, I never heard either sun or moon mentioned in any stories or myths.

[3] Dr. Merriam, the eminent zoologist, confirmed me in my opinion that the California Indians got their dogs rather recently, from other tribes (who presumably got theirs by European importation, like the horse).

argued and argued about it, the old men, the chiefs, did. This is the year we have to repeat the midwinter moon. No, it's next year. No, we did it three years ago. Ah, you don't know, you are too old, you are mixed up. We young fellows, we used to laugh listening to the old men argue. . . . Yes, Doc, the winters used to drag in the old-time *astsuy*. That's the time when you tell long stories, stories of long ago, *dilansini'qi* we call it. About Coyote, and Silver Fox, and Lizard, them all they used to be people, long long ago."

It was at about this time that I became acquainted with that "gambling" that I had been hearing so much about and which seemed to play such a part in Pit River life. It had puzzled me, for instance, to hear Jack Folsom lamenting the death of one of his sons a few years back, in these terms: "Yes, he was a fine boy, a good worker, never made any trouble, HE WAS A GOOD GAMBLER. . . ." Well, now I was going to have a chance to observe it; there was going to be an Indian big-time at Tulu'kuupi, there would be lots of gambling. I had always thought of gambling as dice or roulette or fan-tan or what-have-you in man's everlasting effort to beat the mathematical laws of chance. And I could see that like all hoary manifestations of human imbecility, it would always attract the charlatans and the crooks and the sharks, the whole setup which is associated in our minds with the words gambling and gambler. I was trying to fit that into the Indian picture; it didn't fit. . . .

Tulu'kuupi, the "sack," the end of the valley. Indians were converging from everywhere, in buggies, on horseback, in wagons, and a few in rickety-rackety automobiles held up with bale-wire. Campfires everywhere in the sagebrush. There must have been a hundred or two hundred Indians. Greetings. Where is So-and-So? He is camped over there, under that juniper. . . . They say Wa'wa Eliyu is going to act as main chief. . . . Aw, he is too old. . . . The Paiutes have sent a team of good gamblers. And the Modocs, too. Some of our people are drunk already, the dam-fools, them Paiutes don't drink when they are playing hand-game, they'll beat us again. . . . I went around with Jack Folsom. He had more knowledge of modern ways than most of the older men, and it made him a sort of "chief." I knew quite a few Indians, from my previous experience as a cowboy in that country—and Jack introduced me to others: "He is all right. He is not a white man. He is Spanish." (In that part of the country, Spanish meant "Mexican," just riffraff to the white overlords of the ranches, only one degree above the Indians, who were on the level of horses and cattle.)

Evening had hardly set in when the rattle of sticks was heard, clack-clack-clack-clack-clack . . . and people began converging from all over the camp toward that spot. A hand-game had started between a team of Paiutes on one side, and a mixed team of Modocs and Pit Rivers on the other.

Between them was a campfire. The men of each team were kneeling in a row—in front of them a long plank, just a board. The Paiutes at the moment "had the bones." So they were singing, and except for two of them who were hiding the bones, they all were beating on the board in front of them with short sticks. That was the clack-clack-clack I had heard. It was about as fast in time as the ticking of a watch. It was as uniform in time as a metronome, *and there was no beat*. The melody was a typical Paiute gambling-song, a short melody of four phrases, starting rather high and cascading down in intervals of a whole tone or a tone-and-a-half. They used the "closed throat" method of singing. There was no connection between the time of the clack-clack-clack and the time of the melody.

There they were singing away, the Paiutes were, and two of them were hiding the bones. The naked bone, and the tied bone. The tied bone has a string tied around its middle. You guess for the naked bone. But, if you are the guesser, you try to fool your enemy. You try to read his mind. You make melodramatic gestures. You point to the right, you point to the left, you point to the middle (with palm perpendicular), you point to the outside (there are *two* pairs of bones, remember, both naked bones might be outside). You try to remember this Paiute fellow's gambling habit, he always hides the naked bone in his left, and just as you say: "Ha," he shifts. You, you shifted them. You are supposed to turn your palms out. I did. No, you didn't. Yes I did. Where is the chief? He is drunk. Oh, what the hell, why don't you fellows play, you always argue—. . . These sons-of-bitches *pahaqmaali* Paiutes, that fellow there . . . No, he is Modoc. . . . You are crazy, him a *lutuaami?* You are crazy, he is my, I call him *malis*. He is my brother-in-law. *Malis,* that's fire. So there is an argument started. Clack-clack-clack-clack at it again. The Modocs are hiding the bones, now. The Paiutes are guessing. They don't quarrel among themselves. They pull down their hats over their eyes. The Modocs and Pit Rivers are singing. They swing their bodies from left to right, in the rhythm of the song. But they are not swaying just right. Something is wrong. Two of them are very drunk. The Paiutes are putting their heads together, whispering, with their hats pulled over their eyes. Somebody throws a bunch of twigs on the fire. It blazes up. All the Paiutes grab their hats and shield their eyes. There is one fellow who seems to be their leader. He has a very dark face. His hair is down to his shoulders. They all are whispering to him. He leans over, listening to them. Sometimes he nods. The Modocs and Pit Rivers are getting a little bit out of hand. Two drunken fellows try to horn in. Suddenly they change their song. It falters for a while and dies away in the sagebrush. Everybody laughs. An old woman gets up and spits and goes to her camp in the darkness. Campfires everywhere around. People cooking. Smell of bacon. People calling across. "How is the game?" "Them Paiutes are winning. Our people are drunk. They have no luck, anyhow!"

That Paiute man starts. He claps his hands, then he spreads them apart. He is on his knees. Then he brings the hands together, slowly. He is pointing to the middle (both naked bones inside). One of the Pit Rivers shifts his bones. Everybody laughs. The Paiutes never laugh. They are very different people, full of the desert. An old woman cackles, back of the firelight. Now both players on the Modoc-Pit River combination get nervous and shift their bones. The Paiute man says: HA! and he points with an outstretched hand. Both Pit River-Modocs throw their bones across, laughing. A man bends over and pulls one of the markers and sticks it in the ground on the Paiute side. Everybody yells. He looks confused. "The bones are on that side. What's the matter with you?" He scoots out of sight. Now the Paiutes have the bones. . . .

I stirred in my sleep. The camp was quiet. Just a few babies crying here and there, but the game was going on, clack-clack-clack-clack, out there where the campfire was flickering and black shadows of men moving against it.

We were camped there nearly a week, playing hand-game, making speeches, long-winded speeches. Those speeches of the old men! You don't have to listen to them. Why do the young men sit there on the ground, listening with mouths agape? Nobody obliges them, no pressure of public opinion (there is very little public condemnation for anyone's sins, among the Pit Rivers, they are simply tolerant), then why do all the people, men, women, young men, even little boys, gather around, sit on the ground. Those speeches of the old men, those long-winded speeches!! They always start at the beginning of the world, literally: ". . . and then Silver Fox said to Coyote . . ." and it goes on and on and on. All the verbs are put in the remote past conjugation, with the ending in *−uaasa* or *−iaasa*. And then *kuan tsikuaasa dzeemul*. And then Coyote he didn't *−aasa* know what to answer. And if the white people get enough of us Indians to sign that paper for Washington, we will be like Coyote and we will *−aasa* lose the rest of our lands, etc., etc., etc. for hours. Then the people move over to another old man. He is a Pit River by birth, but he was brought up by the Klamath Indians (who are first cousins to the Pit Rivers), and while there he came under the influence of two movements: the Indian Shakers and the Christian Missionaries (the C. M. failed utterly with the Pit Rivers, they didn't even get to first base). Now he starts. His speech is quite nonpolitical. It has to do with religion and Jesus. He speaks by turns in Pit River and in English: "This here Jesus, he and his wife Mary, and they had a little boy with them, they traveled all over the world, they made mountains and trees, they made trees, they made springs everywhere, *teeqaade toolol*. . . . This here Jesus he was a great man; he was the best gambler in the whole United States!" The Modocs weren't listening to him much; there were no Paiutes in the audience. Almost all the listeners were Pit Rivers. There were no jeers, no heckling, just a lot of brown faces squinting in the sun. When he was finished, mopping his brow, they moved over to where another hand-game had started, all women. There was a big Modoc woman. Nobody could guess her. She hid the bones in a bandanna handkerchief. While she sang she shook her big fat body, sitting on the ground, swaying from side to side with the rhythm of the song. Then she would whip her hands out with the handkerchief still in one hand. The guesser would yell "Ha." She would laugh, show the bones, and throw them in the air. They always guessed her wrong.

It was dawn, and everybody was stirring all over the camp. Some early wagons were already departing. Business of packing, gathering baskets, harnessing or saddling horses, calling scampering children. I was saddling my horse, talking to Jack Folsom. A man came to us. He was the same surly fellow who had received my visit so badly some time before. I had noticed him watching me closely around camp several times, but I never spoke to him and he never spoke to me. This man now came to me, and he put a beautiful little buckskin bag embroidered with beads into my hands, and he said: "My wife made this for you." Then he just turned on his heel and was gone. I stood there, sort of dumbfounded. Jack Folsom looked at the bag and said: "That's nice bag, Doc, that's good work." "Who is that fellow, Jack?" "I don't know him, Doc. I think he comes from down the river."

From there I went back with Jack and Lena to their shack tucked away in the sagebrush, behind a hill not far from Alturas.

We took up the study of language again, and went out in the brush with his rifle to shoot jackrabbits (hares) for the cooking pot. There were hundreds and hundreds of them, darting from every bush. In a minute or two we would bag one, which was enough for the three of us. Then we would sit down and talk and talk. . . . "Jack, have you got a *dinihowi?*" Jack looked at me, squinting a smile: "Where did you learn that word, Doc?"—"Oh, here and there, Blind Hall. . . ." Jack snorted. "That old bastard hasn't got any *dinihowis*. They wouldn't live with his poisons. You want to know what that old man does with *dinihowis?* He steals them, just like he steals other doctors' *damaagomes*. He steals honest Indians' *dinihowis* but he can't keep them. They won't live with his poisons. When he wants to get a woman he goes into the brush and he calls for a lice from her. . . ." "For a what?" "For a lice. Them things crawl around between your legs." "Oh, a louse." "I dunno. I always heard white people call them lice. We say *a'mits*. Lots of Indians got them. So this Hall goes into the bush, and he has his *a'mits* to call for her *a'mits*. And pretty soon the woman get up from her campfire, she don't know why but she go wandering into the sagebrush and old Hall is there waiting for her."

"But Jack, that lice is not her *damaagome!*" "How the hell do I know it ain't her *damaagome*. It might be her *dinihowi*. I didn't say it was her *damaagome*."

"No, that's right, I made a mistake. I meant her *dinihowi*."

"I didn't say it was her *dinihowi*. Lots of us got them lice between our legs."

I shut up. Jack was a very kind man, but whenever I seemed stupid he would sort of lose his temper and get cross and squint across the hills. I had learned the weather signals. So I shut up.

We were still sitting in the same spot. Jack says, out of the blue: "Yes, I got a *dinihowi*. Must be a damn poor Indian without a *dinihowi*. When I was a young fellow, old people always get after us. You go get luck for yourself, You can't live without luck. Go and run up the mountain in the afternoon. Try to beat the sun, the

red light, to the top, get there first. Keep your breath. Run steady.
. . . You know, Doc, I used to be a good runner. We used to have
foot-races in the old-time days. All the young Indians we used to
try beat each other going from one place to another, maybe five
mile, maybe ten mile. Run through the sagebrush, keep your
breath in, don't slow down, don't sit down and sleep, don't get
scared, keep running through the brush, sometimes awful high
brush, higher than your head. . . . I was pretty good runner in
them days. Now I make my race-horses run. . . . Well, the old
people kept after me. You beat the sun to the top of the mountain,
then you'll be a man. I tried, and I tried. Then one day a big frog
was standing in the road, right in the dust of the trail. He says:
You'll never get to the top without me helping you. I been
watching you. It's awful how hard you try. I'll help you. . . ."

"Did you get to the top that day?"

"Yes, I got to the top. There ain't nothing there."

"Then what?"

"Then I came down."

"Oh. . . ."

"What do you mean, oh? I got my *dinihowi,* didn't I? I am
always trying to tell you things, Doc, but you are worse than a
young Indian."

We came back through the brush. He was wiping the barrel
of the gun with a rope with a rag tied to it. I was carrying the hare
of the day by the long ears. Lena was sitting in front of the shack.
That woman was truly enormous. She was at her eternal beadwork. She looked up at us and smiled. Then she went back to her
beads. I laid the hare in front of the campfire. Jack said, "Better
draw it, Doc. We'll have it for supper. I am going out to look for
them horses." Those were wonderful quiet days with Jack and
Lena, in that little corner of sagebrush behind the turn of the hill.

But it was only a few days before Jack got restless again. He
had some race-horses he had loaned to a fellow in Hat Creek.
They were colts. He had to keep an eye on them. He didn't trust
that fellow. Off they went again, in the spring-wagon, we pushed

and hoisted and drug Lena into the wagon-bed where she sat enthroned amidst her many baskets. Jack got into the driver's seat, released the brakes. I didn't have time to say goodby even. He had hitched up a colt with an old horse. The old horse started. The colt bucked. Down came the black snake over his buttocks. They were off and the wagon almost tipped, Lena was holding onto the sides, smiling. Jack turned his face around once. He was grinning and he yelled something, but I didn't catch what he said.

I stayed there that night, but in the morning I went.

2

I was up again, the next year. This time I had a jalopy, myself. Progress. You can't defend yourself against progress. So this time I came up following the Pit River from Redding up. I was meeting more and more Indians after Montgomery Creek. I had never been through that territory before, only once, years before with a drove of horses, through a snowstorm. I didn't even recognize the country.

I got into the upper land. It was getting dark. I had a wolfish-looking bitch swaying on the back, on top of my camping stuff. I was getting tired driving that damned car. I hate them. When I got to Big Valley I couldn't stand the driving over the rough road any more. I saw a campfire a little south of the road. I was awfully tired. I thought: They must be Indians.

I got out and walked over, being careful to make a noise. There was no need for care. There comes Sukmit: "I have been watching for you. I got lonesome for you. I sent my poison after you. The old woman is there, in the camp. Old lady Gordon died. The other woman, my uncle, she is dead. We are all going to die. We can't help it. What have you got there? Is that a coyote? Looks like a coyote. Don't growl at me, you son-of-a-bitch, I am Indian doctor. I ain't afraid of you. Want to be my poison? Say, Jaime, did you get my message? I got lonesome for you. You want to be a doctor? I teach you. I am Indian doctor. I teach you, pretty bad, get scared, I teach you, you no white man. . . ."

Under this avalanche I was being dragged across some wasteland toward the campfire I had seen. There were no introductions of any kind whatever. Nobody paid any attention to me at all. I sat in a corner. I said nothing. Then a little boy brought me a basket full of some kind of mush, and it had salt in it, too. I was reserved and very careful, keeping out of the way, in the outer light of the fire. Then Mary's chuckle came out of the darkness (I hadn't seen her until that moment, sitting there beyond the firelight): "Ha-ha, you white man."

I followed that bunch for several weeks. I never saw such a goddam lot of improbable people. Sukmit was the only acknowledged shaman, but he wasn't a leader. He was no chief, no *weheelu,* among them. We went around the brush. We would stop anywhere, evidently by common consent. We would stop in the brush. Always there was a spring near by. I never knew where we were going. We were going somewhere. I didn't care at all. We were going somewhere, maybe. And if we were not going somewhere, we were not going, that's all. In the evening we would make a fire, several fires (there were several families of us). In the morning we moved again. I don't know where we were going. I don't think the Indians knew. We made quite a procession through the sagebrush, about six or seven of us, my car usually tagging at the end. I didn't know where we were going, nobody seemed to know where we were going, and then the night would settle on us, the fires would die down. The coyotes would begin barking from out in the brush. The Indians' dogs would howl back. Then everything would smolder back into the darkness.

Then one morning I was made to realize that there was something wrong about the white man's conception of the "taciturn" Indian. That happened the next day. We were going along the sagebrush, no road, just sagebrush, wind left, wind right, avoid this big clump, here's bad one, bump into the ditch . . . but there is no road at all anywhere, you are going through the brush, bumpety-bump, all of us, six, seven, maybe eight cars, eight tin lizzies rattling through the sagebrush. Then, one morning, we had to stop. One of the tin lizzies was on the blink, and everybody got out to help. Then I witnessed something that amazed me. I had made up my mind that these men were straight out of the old Stone Age. I myself am not a mechanic; I hate machines; I am all thumbs; I don't understand machines; horses, yes; machines, no. And here I was watching these Stone Age men unscrew and rescrew and take things apart or out of the engine and spread them on a piece of canvas on the ground . . . but the amazing thing to me was their argumentation. It was perfectly logical. ". . . Can't be the ignition, look, I get a spark . . . I tell you, it's in the transmission . . . Now pull that lever . . ." Maybe I was over-impressed because the simplest machine smells of magic to me. Maybe I missed a lot of their argument because off and on they would lapse into Pit River. They called the battery *hadatsi* "heart"; a wheel is *pi'nine* (a hoop used in the old days for target practice); and so on and so forth. But certainly they made use of logic just as any white man would. Finally the engine, or whatever was wrong, was repaired. Then I overheard one young fellow say to another: "You know why this happened? Because he has been sleeping with his woman while she was menstruating! That's against the rules."

At last everything was fixed: the engine put together again, everything rescrewed . . . but the trek of the tin lizzies was not resumed. We just stayed there.

I don't know why we stayed there. We just stayed there, in the middle of nowhere, in the middle of the sagebrush. After that car which had broken down had been repaired, I naturally expected that everybody would get back into their cars, and the procession be resumed. But no, nobody got back into the cars; everybody was drifting around, sitting here, sitting there, gossiping, yawning.

I asked a man: "Are we going on, or do we camp here?" He answered: "I dunno. I am not the chief. Ask that old man over there." I went to the old man over there. He said he was not the chief. Ask that fellow over there. That fellow over there was a middle-aged man. He said: "Hell, I am not the one to say, I am not a chief!" "Well, who is a chief here?" "I dunno. That old man over there, I guess. He is old enough to have the say. Go and ask him." That old man over there was the same old man over there, and he gave me the same treatment. He was no chief. Who said he was a chief? They could start when they liked, when they jolly well liked, he didn't care, he didn't even know where they were going, where the hell were they going, did they know where they were going, did I know where they were going?? . . . He sat on the foot-board of one of the cars. He was squinting into the afternoon sun; it was late afternoon, by then. He was chewing tobacco and spitting the brown juice. He paid no more attention to me and went back to his reverie, squinting into the sun.

I noticed a woman had started a campfire. Very soon another one did likewise. So I went to my car and drove it next to Suk-mit's. Old Mary was sitting on the ground in the shade of the car, weaving a rough basket of willow twigs. "Where is Sukmit?" *"Tsesuwi diimas'adi,* I don't know, went off in the brush some place, that boy is crazy, *yalu'tuusi,* always looking for *da-maagomes;* you bring me firewood, white man, I cook." "All right."

The sun was going down. I heard two or three shots, off in the sagebrush. I made our fire. There were four or five other campfires. A man came by; he had several hares by the ears; he tossed one over to us. Mary drew it, threw the guts to my bitch, hacked it in four pieces, and stuck these on sticks to broil over the fire. No sight of Sukmit. We ate. Then Mary told me an old-time story. I spread my blankets on the ground. I rolled a cigarette and watched the stars. Some coyotes started a howling, not far off. My bitch stood up, all bristles, and she howled back (in answering coyotes, most dogs howl instead of barking). I went to sleep with my head full of old-time stories, tin lizzies, *damaagomes* mixed up with engines, coyotes and sagebrush.

I was awakened by the usual quarrel between Sukmit and his mother. The smell of coffee was in the air. We ate. I observed the camp. There were no preparations for starting. Everybody lolling around. Mary took up her basket and kept on weaving. Another woman went to the spring with a bucket (there was a spring, nearby; of course they must have known). A man was tinkering with his car. Another one went off into the brush with his gun. That old man, the supposed "chief," was going around poking at things with a stick. He was almost blind. The morning was drawing on. I took out my notebook and started working on linguistics.

The days went by. Not so many days, but four, five days, maybe. I don't remember exactly. I was not taking notes. I was living. Sagebrush. Old-time stories, hares cooking over the fire, slow gossip, So-and-So is poisoning So-and-So, I don't believe it, yes he is, how do you know, well his paternal aunt belongs to the *hammaawi,* and they poisoned his *apau.* "That doesn't make him related!" "Who said related? I didn't say related. I said they poisoned him." . . . The days went by, four, five, six days.

Then it happened. It was midday, or near. I heard a man say, way off: "*S.huptsiidizima.*" If he had said *lhuptiidza toolol,* "Let's all go," it would have been different. But no, it was not in the imperative mode, it was in the indicative: "We are going, all of us, *toolol,* we are going, *s.huptsiidizima,* we are all going." He didn't say: LET'S ALL GO! No, he merely stated a fact: WE ARE ALL GOING.

It was like a whirlwind. I turned around. Women were throwing baskets into the tin lizzies. Then without any further warning or consultation one of the tin lizzies started off in a cloud of dust. Another was right on its heels. Then a third one, but this one had hardly started when someone yelled, "Hey! you are forgetting your baby!!" The car backed, a young woman jumped out and ran to a juniper tree where the baby was sleeping in the cradle-board swinging under a branch; she slung the cradle-board over her shoulder and ran back to the car, laughing and laughing; everybody was laughing; then the car started again.

Sukmit yelled at me: *"Lhupta,* let's go! For Christ's sake, are you going to stay here forever?!" I picked up my papers and ran for my own car. . . . We go, we go, we wind in and out, all afternoon, all the cars more or less following each other, we skirted the town of Alturas, never stopped, we were going north, the sun went down, there was a moon, we kept going, somehow or other no car broke down, not even a flat tire, we had luck with us, and toward morning we stopped on those flats by Davis Creek. . . .

I was going back to Berkeley. I wasn't going to be caught by the fall, much less by the winter (it goes down to minus 30 Fahrenheit all over the plateau, Alturas, Susanville, Lakeview). I said to Sukmit: "Let's go down southward. I have a camping place there in Berkeley. It's close to San Francisco." "Yes, I have heard of that place. Lots of people, they say." "Well, let's go, *lhepta,* you and me." "No, not *lhepta, lhupta.* We are not going home, we are going away from home. I have told you that a million times already. It's no use trying to teach a white man." "I am going to my home," I yelled. "My home, that's *septa,* isn't it?" "No, it isn't *septa.* That would mean that you are on your way. You are sitting here, ain't you? You are not *septa,* you are *taptegudzii.* . . ." The old lady called over from the fire: "What you two arguing about again? You all the time the two of you arguing like two old men! You white man he Indian, ha-ha-ha. . . ."

We sit down under that tall pine tree, and eat. We are still quarreling, Sukmit and I. "How can you go southward and leave your *damaagome* behind you?" "He can find me, can't he? I can sing his song. He'll hear it. Just like 'lectricity, goes under ground, anywhere I can call my *damaagome,* he comes. . . ." Old Mary looks up. "He never come . . ." she says. Sukmit flares into a rage at her. "He come! He come! He come!" He is stamping around her. He is in a perfect rage. He is shaking both fists over her head. She says: "He never come."

I was sort of upset, even shocked, by this childish behavior, this tantrum, on his part. There he was the powerful shaman, the tamer of *damaagomes, trépignant autour de sa mère,* shaking his fists over her head, shouting: "They'll come! They'll come when I call them, goddam it they'll come!!" The old lady was sitting on the ground weaving her basket. She smiled; she kept repeating calmly: "They won't come . . . too far . . . they can't hear you."

After a while he calmed down. I proposed to record some songs on my phonograph machine. I carried around one of those old Edison phonographs with a big horn. You made the records on wax cylinders with a special cutting jewel needle; then to play them you changed to a needle with a rounded point. The whole contraption was crude and primitive compared to modern methods. It was hard enough to operate in a laboratory; imagine it in the open, competing with the wind; the horn would swing around; we cursed. . . . How I sweated and labored over those Indian songs, and the fortune I spent on broken records! . . . That was before the days of amplification; later on new methods appeared; flat disks, unbreakable and permanent; wonderful improvements . . . but the Indians are gone, no more singing to record.[4]

Sukmit had a powerful voice of which he was vain. He was delighted to sing into the horn and then hear his own voice thrown back at him. We recorded several songs, mostly gambling songs and some puberty-dance songs. Then he said: "Let's record Old Blind Hall's medicine-song, you know, that one about digging up wild turnips and they all are rotten." So we put that on. It goes something like this:

At Dalmo'ma near the spring

---

[4]The University would not help me; took no interest; would not even give me enough money to have the records transcribed and made permanent on modern disks. Decent anthropoligists don't associate with drunkards who go rolling in ditches with shamans.

I dig for wild turnips
At Dalmo'ma in the evening
I turn up but rotten ones.

Then I said to him: "Sukmit, let's record one of your own medicine-songs." The old lady had heard me, and she cried from where she was sitting at the campfire. "Don't do it, Sukmit, don't do it, Sukmit, don't do it, *tse-dutsee, tse-dutsee!!*" He seemed dubious, torn two ways by his vanity and his fear of possible consequences. "See, suppose I put my song in the machine; now you go to Berkeley; sometime you play my song; my *damaagome* he hear it, he say: Ha! my father is calling me, I'd better go and find him, maybe he needs me. . . . So he come here to Berkeley, strange place, maybe he get lost, maybe somebody steal him . . . then I get sick, maybe I die. . . ." "Aw! he couldn't hear that phonograph all the way from Alturas!" "Sure he can! Just like 'lectricity, it goes underground, but it don't need no wires."[5] "What do you know about electricity?! Electricity doesn't work that way!" "Hell, what do you know about *damaagomes*? You are nothing but a white man, a goddam tramp."[6] "No, I am not a white man!" "Yes, you are a white man, you are a white man forever!!"

Old Mary chuckled from over the campfire "You two always quarreling like two old men. You Indian, you white man, ha-ha-ha! You both crazy!"

So I took them down to Berkeley in my auto, Sukmit and old Mary (she once told me her Indian name; it had something to do with tule reeds at dawn; but I never heard any one call her by it; Sukmit called her *niini,* baby-talk for *nen* "mother"; and I also

---

[5]This was before the days of wireless (at least before wireless became common knowledge)—an interesting example of so-called "primitive mentality."

[6]The Pit Rivers call the whites *enellaaduwi,* literally "wanderer," from the verbal root *−llaa−* "to wander," plus the adverbial suffix *−duw−* "around." What struck the Pit Rivers most about the first whites (prospectors, trappers, etc.) was that they appeared to be homeless.

Sukmit in Berkeley

called her that after a while; other Indians called her "aunt," or "sister-in-law on the brother's side," which is *wattulaawi,* or whatever the relationship term if they were related; if not related to her they just called her *wiya'tsaale,* which is equivalent to "old lady").

The city was a great disappointment to Sukmit. Didn't interest him at all. "Too many people crawling around just like ants—makes me crazy. . . ." He spent most of his time wandering in the hills back of the University campus. He looked sad and dejected. He didn't quarrel any more.

One day I said to him: "Sukmit, I know what's troubling you. . . . You have been wandering in the hills and calling your *damaagomes,* and they don't hear you!" He looked at me and I thought he was going to burst into tears. "Yes," he said, "you and *niini,* you were right; they don't hear me; they don't come! I am going to die if I stay here."

So I sent them back on the train. Funny-looking pair they made at the station, bewildered, he with his long hair and his black sombrero, his long arms and his hump; she clutching a bundle; and her gray hair under a bright silk handkerchief we had just bought for her.

I spoke a word to the conductor for them. He smiled broadly; "Sure I'll take care of them. I know Indians. I was raised in Oklahoma."

As the train pulled out, old Mary gave me the Pit River goodby: *Is tus'i taakaadzee,* Man, live well! *Ittu toolol hakaadzi-gudzuma,* We also will live.

3

I went up north again the next summer. I found Jack Folsom and Lena at their place behind the little hill in the sagebrush. I noticed that Lena seemed apathetic, ill. Jack was as usual, with his quizzical smile, his quiet ways, his practical sense. "Say, Doc, I hear your friend Sukmit is around. There is a woman sick near town, Indians live there, well, there is a woman sick there, some doctor poisoned her, and they got your friend Sukmit to doctor her . . . and say, Doc, we are pretty near out of grub, you will be in town in two minutes with your car, today is Saturday and the stores will be open late, and will you bring back some grub, get some bacon, and bring some sweets for Lena, she loves sweets, I don't know what's the matter with that woman, Doc, something's wrong, she don't look well to me." "All right, Jack."

So I went to Alturas, did the shopping, and on the way back, it was dusk, I saw the familiar figure of Sukmit, a little way off the road, walking through the brush with long strides. I stopped the car, and honked and yelled. He paid no attention. I honked and yelled again. Surely he must hear me. I got out of the car and went up to him. He had heard me all right, and he was in a towering rage: "Goddam you, I am fixing for a doctoring! I have caught a new *damaagome* and I am training him, he is wild yet, he was following me like a dog, and here you come yelling your head off, you scared him away!" "I am sorry, Sukmit, I didn't know. . . ." "You never know anything. You'll never learn anything, you'll never be an Indian, you'll always be a damfool white man!!" "All right, all right, you don't have to be so nasty about it," and I turned to go. He followed me: "Well, aren't you going to give me a ride? They are waiting for me, I have to doctor a sick woman." "What's the use if I scared your *damaagome*?" "Do you think I have only one *damaagome*? That's just a new one I am training."

So I took him to the place. There were a dozen or so Indians gathered around a campfire. There was a woman lying under a blanket on a bed of tules on the ground. Old Mary was there. She greeted me with her usual banter: "Here is the Indian white man. He is going to do the interpreting. No, maybe he'll do the doctoring. Ha-ha-ha. Indian white man." Most of the Indians already knew me. Greetings. *"Is kaakaadzi,* Man, you are alive, *is kaakaadzi.* Where have you been? Where is your wife, your son, *mi'mu amiteudzan, mi'mu belatsi?* Why didn't they come?"

Sukmit looked somber and abstracted. He went and looked at the sick woman silently; then he came back and knelt in front of the fire. Old Mary then got up and went a little way into the sagebrush and called the *damaagomes.*[7] Everybody became silent. Then Sukmit started one of his songs. Two or three people caught on, then others, then nearly everybody. Then he clapped his hands and the singing stopped abruptly. Now he is interpellating a poison, and old Mary, his mother, interprets (that is, repeats word for word, but more slowly, although Sukmit never got himself into a state of *bafouillage,* like Blind Hall and some others). And so on and so forth. In between interpellations of the poisons there was the usual relaxing and smoking by the audience and the usual gossip. But Sukmit never relaxed. He became more and more somber and abstracted. To me he seemed to be getting exhausted. After a while of this he got up and "sucked" the sick woman: he put his lips to different parts of her body and sucked with a strong hissing noise. Then he came back and knelt again in front of the fire, right next to me. He looked very sick. He asked for a container. Somebody passed him an empty can that had contained lard (a three-pound can), and he puked and puked and puked into it. I was right next to him. What he puked looked exactly like very dark blood, but the light was uncertain. He made

---

[7]After the *damaagomes* have been called, no one is allowed to approach the meeting, whether Indian or white man. The reason is obvious: the sudden arrival of a stranger might scare away the *damaagomes* hovering in the air over the shaman's head.

a grimace and said to me: "Fuahh! . . . it looks like coffee." He was still retching. He poured the can into the fire.[8]

Most of the Indians then left. Old Mary looked very tired also. She said to me: "You take care of your Sukmit," and she disappeared. Sukmit was like a drunken man. I spread my blankets on the ground and dragged him in after me. For a long time he was crying like a child, and shaking all over. Finally he went to sleep.

In the morning he was quite all right. So also was the sick woman (she evidently had had a bad case of "funk"). She came to where we were having breakfast, and she gave Sukmit a string of beads for payment. She said: "It's not much but I am a poor woman." Sukmit took the string and threw it to his mother, and he said to the woman: "That's good. I am not doing it for payment." Then Sukmit pumped up his tires and he and old Mary started for Big Valley (which was their home), and I went back to Jack and Lena at their place in the sagebrush around the little hill.

Poor Lena was really sick. Jack would have liked to call in Blind Hall, but he was away somewhere down river. Then we heard that a bunch of Modocs were in town on their way to their home in Oregon, and with them was old Kate, a famous medicine-woman, and Jack decided to try her. She arrived in the afternoon, in a horse-wagon, with her son, a big strapping fellow (with whom I later studied the Modoc language). She was a little bit of an old woman, so *racroquevillée* that she was almost bent double; she was nearly blind; still she insisted on "helping" (all the conversation had to be in English, since the Modocs didn't understand Pit River, and vice versa) with the cooking. She would totter around, extend a claw, peer, grab something and drop it in the skillet. Jessie (Jack's daughter by another wife—and

---

[8]The can looked about half full. Was it an intestinal hemorrhage of hysterical origin? Sukmit (unlike some of the shamans, Old Modoc Kate, for instance, of whom I will speak later) was incapable of *supercherie*. I can vouch for that. I knew him too well. When two boon companions get drunk together time and time again, the truth is bound to come out. I simply have no explanation for the stuff in that can except the one given above.

a big, handsome woman Jessie was, somewhere around in her forties, graceful, dignified, a little bit haughty), who had come to help,[9] Jessie would sigh, turn her face aside to grimace, then calmly remove whatever *immondice* old Kate had dropped into the skillet.

Evening arrived. Old Kate had a sister who acted as her "interpreter," a much younger woman. Everything was ready; we were all inside the cabin; still old Kate was waiting for something; finally she said: "Dat white man going to stay?" "He is no white man!" said Jack. "He is Indian just like us." "What tribe?" she asked me. "Spanish," I answered. "Oh, dat's all right. Spanish good people." To her, too, Spanish meant Mexican.

Old Kate's procedure was slightly different from Blind Hall, Sukmit, or the other Pit River shamans I have associated with; but on the whole it followed the same lines—perhaps a little less loose, a trifle more conventionalized. For instance, her songs appeared to be directed less to an individual *damaagome* than to a generalized animal. Her sister would explain to me: "That's duck song . . . that's crane song . . . that's pelican song. . . ." The old woman's son had gone out. Doctoring didn't interest him. The Pit Rivers didn't know that kind of singing and were too self-conscious to try. Only the old woman's sister carried on the singing. Old Kate complained. Finally she turned to me: "Why you no sing? *Canta, canta!*" "All right, I'll try." The songs weren't difficult. They had more lilt than the Pit River ones. Anyhow, the important thing was to make a noise and be heard by the poisons.

Toward midnight or one o'clock (unlike the Pit River shamans, who never doctor for more than a couple of hours, Kate kept it up all night, right till dawn—although all the Pit Rivers had fallen asleep in various corners), Kate had a fit. She started to shake, foam at the mouth, and throw herself around. At first her sister tried to hold her down, but she wasn't strong enough. She

---

[9]Lena had raised Jessie, but they must have been almost the same age, at most ten years' difference—so Jessie looked upon Lena as her mother.

called for help to the Pit Rivers; but for some reason no one moved. Then she yelled at me: "Hey, you Mexican, hold her, I'll call her son. . . ." He came in, a calm, big, powerful fellow. Yet, with the two of us sitting on her she managed once to free herself, that little bit of an old woman whom ordinarily you could have pushed over with your little finger! After a while she quieted down, and the singing started again, at intervals. But she was tired. Once she peered at the roof: "Is dat morning?" "No, Kate, it's the moon. There is a crack in the roof." She sighed.

Finally she started to extract the poison. She sucked and sucked. Then she straightened up, put her hand to her mouth, and grabbed something that was between her teeth. In the light of the lamp I saw distinctly what she did: she bit a piece of her own fingernail off. This she exhibited around as the poison. Then she called for a bowl of water; she drowned the poison in it and threw the water in a corner of the room.

In the morning the Modocs started to go. Jack Folsom wanted to give Kate some money, but she refused it, "I didn't do any good, Jack, you people don't sing, my poison no hear. Your woman going to die. Too bad." She said goodby to me. "You good man, Spanish, you help, you sing. Come see me my place Oregon." I said I would.

(I did go there, the next year, to study the Modoc language with her son. I had many talks with her. One day I was sitting on a log in the sun beside her; she was smoking her pipe; I said: "Kate, you remember that time at Jack Folsom's place when you doctored that woman. . . . You bit off your fingernail and said it was the poison. . . ." She gave me a side-long look, pretty piercing in spite of her rheumy eyes; she grumbled: ". . . You know too much—sure dat's tomfoolery, good for people, make him believe—but my poison him no fool, him powerful, no nonsense, but he no hear dat time, son-of-a-bitch!" ". . . Kate, why did you become a doctor?" "Oh, long time ago, me young girl, go in woods look for berries, I no look for poison, poison find me." "Did he scare you?" "You bet he scare me!" "Does he still scare you when he comes?" She burst into her cackling laughter: "Hell NO! He don't scare me. I scare him now!!!")

Soon after the Modocs left, Lena's own father arrived from Hat Creek country. His name was Jack Wilson. He drove in in a horse-wagon, and with him was an "elder brother" (or cousin) of his, who must have been close to ninety or a hundred; Jack Folsom (who didn't know his own age by years) said of Bob-Chief, or Tom-Chief (like all Indians he had a variety of American names): "When I was a young fellow that old man had already buried three wives." He was still erect, but walked slowly; his skin was the color of chocolate; a few long white whiskers made him look like a walrus.

Jack Wilson was a "sort of doctor," according to Jack Folsom. He would doctor his own daughter, that night. Old Tom-Chief would interpret. Jack Wilson was a tall man, very silent. During the day Tom-Chief, who usually sat on a log, would totter into the sagebrush and make a sort of speech. "What is he doing?" I asked Jack. "Oh, he is telling old-time stories, what the people used to do long ago." "But there is nobody there. To whom is he talking?" Jack shrugged his shoulders: "To the sagebrush, I guess."

When evening came, old Tom-Chief went out and called the *damaagomes*. Three young Indians had arrived; but they were slightly drunk. They sang a *contre-temps* and laughed. Jack had to reprimand them. Old Tom was very deaf; he didn't hear what the doctor said; so everybody had to shout at him what the shaman had said so he could repeat it; the whole thing was a failure. After about an hour Jack Wilson gave up in despair. "No use! My poison don't hear. Mountain lion, wolf, too far away, don't hear!"

In the morning he said to me: "I lost all my children. This the last one. I lose her too."

It was in the afternoon. Autumn and warm. The door of the cabin stood open. Away to the west I could see the hills of sagebrush, silent, and the mountains beyond. One of those days that do not move. There were half a dozen of us in the cabin, and the sick woman breathing heavily on her pile of blankets. I don't know how we all knew it, but we all felt that she was dying just then. At last, Jack Folsom broke down. He buried his face in his hands and started to cry. He cried like a little child, with convulsive sobs. Then that awful sound of the rattle. And even before that had died away Jessie began the wail. Oh, that weird, wild, atrocious thing that goes mounting like the shriek of a wounded beast, that infernal yell drawn away until it falls in a series of exhausted sobs. And again, and again. I was to hear that wail all night through the sagebrush until it drove me mad.

The old man, her father, was kneeling at her head. His face twitched uncontrollably. He closed her eyes, and laid a handkerchief over her face. Then he, too, broke down. He took the head of his child in his lap, he raised it to his breast, and he sobbed and sobbed.

All night long Jessie wandered through the brush, wailing, wailing. And all through the night Indians kept arriving. The men sat against the wall. The women went out into the night and wailed.

One Indian is dead.

Then Jack took his wife's body away to bury it in Hat Creek, her home. He said to me: "I'll be back here in about two weeks, and then we will burn her. Will you stay here for me, Doc?"

I was sort of puzzled about this business of burying first, and burning her after, but I didn't ask him any questions. I said I would stay until he got back. He said: "You sure you won't be scared?" "No, . . . why should I?" "Account of the woman who died." "But why?" "She might come and kill you by mistake." "Hell no!" I said.

The very night after they had left, Wild Bill arrived. He was a horse-breaker by trade and I had known him in the days of my venture in ranching. A delightful fellow, always full of fun and jokes, and a superb rider; in fact he was a crazy daredevil. We had always been friends.

I was surprised to see him. He had tied his horse to a post in the corral and came over to me. He said he had come for the funeral, and that the woman-who-had-died was his cousin. He said "sister."

"How can she be your sister, Bill?"

"Well, she is, Indian way."

"I don't see how."

"Oh, yes. Look: her *apun,* her grandfather on the mother side was the elder brother, what we call *apau,* to my sister, the younger than me, my *enun."*

"But Bill, that doesn't make her your sister!"

"Sure it does, Doc. . . . See, if a man is my wife's brother I call him *malis,* and my own brother, if he is older I call him *apau,* but if he is younger I call him *atun.* Just like my sister, *apis* or *enun.* But if he is my uncle, if he is my father's sister, then I call him. . . . Oh, hell, Doc; you can't get it straight in English. . . . But I tell you, this woman who died she is related to me, I know, because she always called this here Tom-Chief, *aqun,* and he also called me *aqun,* and that proves it."

Wild Bill said he would stay here and wait for Jack Folsom and the rest of the party to come back from the *atsuge* country. That evening he told me a lot about Coyote and the Coyote saga. The Coyote stories form a regular cycle, a saga. This is true of all of California; and it extends eastward even as far as the Pueblos of Arizona and New Mexico. Coyote has a double personality. He is at once the Creator, and the Fool. This antinomy is very important. Unless you understand it you will miss the Indian psychology completely—at least you will miss the significance of their literature (because I call their tales, their "old-time stories," literature).

The wise man and the buffoon: the two aspects of Coyote, Coyote Old Man. Note that I don't call them the good and the evil, because that conception of morality does not seem to play much part in the Pit River attitude to life. Their mores are not much concerned with good and evil. You have a definite attitude toward moral right and moral wrong. I don't think the Pit River has. At least, if he has, he does not try to coerce. I have heard Indians say: "That's not right what he is doing, that fellow. . . ." "What d'you mean it's not right?" ". . . Well . . . you ain't supposed to do things that way . . . it never was done that way . . . there'll be trouble." "Then why don't you stop him?" "Stop him? How can I stop him? It's his way."

The Pit Rivers (except the younger ones who have gone to the Government School at Fort Bidwell) don't ever seem to get a very clear conception of what you mean by the term God. This is true even of those who speak American fluently, like Wild Bill. He said to me: "What is this thing that the white people call God? They are always talking about it. It's goddam this and goddam that, and in the name of the god, and the god made the world. Who is that god, Doc? They say that Coyote is the Indian God, but if I say to them that God is Coyote, they get mad at me. Why?"

"Listen, Bill, tell me. . . . Do the Indians think, really think that Coyote made the world? I mean, do they really think so? Do you really think so?"

"Why of course I do. . . . Why not? . . . Anyway . . . that's what the old people always said . . . only they don't all tell the same story. Here is one way I heard it: it seems like there was nothing everywhere but a kind of fog. Fog and water mixed, they say, no land anywhere, and this here Silver Fox. . . ."

"You mean Coyote?"

"No, no, I mean Silver Fox. Coyote comes later. You'll see, but right now, somewhere in the fog, they say, Silver Fox was wandering and feeling lonely. *Tsikuellaaduwi maandza tsikualaasa.*[10] He was feeling lonely, the Silver Fox. I wish I would meet someone, he said to himself, the Silver Fox did. He was

---

[10]When you tell old-time stories of long ago, every verb must begin with *tsik−*, which then is more or less blended with the pronominal prefix.

walking along in the fog. He met Coyote. 'I thought I was going to meet someone,' he said. The Coyote looked at him, but he didn't say anything. 'Where are you traveling?' says Fox. 'But where are YOU traveling? Why do you travel like that?' 'Because I am worried.'[11] 'I also am wandering,' said the Coyote, 'I also am worrying and traveling.' 'I thought I would meet someone, I thought I would meet someone. Let's you and I travel together. It's better for two people to be traveling together, that's what they always say. . . .'"

"Wait a minute, Bill. . . . Who said that?"

"The Fox said that. I don't know who he meant when he said: *that's what they always say.* It's funny, isn't it? How could he talk about *other* people since there had never been anybody before? I don't know. . . . I wonder about that sometimes, myself. I have asked some of the old people and they say: That's what I have been wondering myself, but that's the way we have always heard it told. And then you hear the Paiutes tell it different! And our own people down the river, they also tell it a little bit different from us. Doc, maybe the whole thing just never happened. . . . And maybe it did happen but everybody tells it different. People often do that, you know. . . ."

"Well, go on with the story. You said that Fox had met Coyote. . . ."

"Oh, yah. . . . Well, this Coyote he says: 'What are we going to do now?' 'What do you think?' says Fox. 'I don't know,' says Coyote. 'Well then,' says Fox, 'I'll tell you: LET'S MAKE THE WORLD.' 'And how are we going to do that?' 'WE WILL SING,' says the Fox.

"So, there they were singing up there in the sky. They were

---

[11]To be worried, *–insimallauw–* (conjugation II). When an Indian is worried, he goes wandering, *–inillaaduw–*. When he is "wandering" he goes around the mountains, cries, breaks pieces of wood, hurls stones. Some of his relatives may be watching him from afar, but they never come near.

singing and stomping[12] and dancing around each other in a circle. Then the Fox he thought in his mind: CLUMP OF SOD, come!! That's the way he made it come: *by thinking*.[13] Pretty soon he had it in his hands. And he was singing, all the while he had it in his hands. They were both singing and stomping. All of a sudden the Fox threw that clump of sod, that *tsapettia*,[14] he threw it down into the clouds. 'Don't look down!' he said to the Coyote. 'Keep on singing! Shut your eyes, and keep them shut until I tell you.' So they kept on singing and stomping around each other in a circle for quite a while. Then the Fox said to the Coyote: 'Now, look down there. What do you see?' 'I see something . . . I see something . . . but I don't know what it is.' 'All right. Shut your eyes again!' Now they started singing and stomping again, and the Fox thought and wished: Stretch! Stretch! 'Now look down again. What do you see?' 'Oh! it's getting bigger!' 'Shut your eyes again and don't look down!' And they went on singing and stomping up there in the sky. 'Now look down again!' 'Oooh! Now it's big enough!' said the Coyote.

"That's the way they made the world, Doc. Then they both jumped down on it and they stretched it some more. Then they made mountains and valleys; they made trees and rocks and everything. It took them a long time to do all that!"

---

[12]Indian dancing is not like the European, by lifting the heels and balancing the body on the toes; on the contrary, one foot is raised *flat* from the ground while the other foot is pressed into the ground (by flexing the knee); then a very slight pause with one foot in the air; then the other foot is stamped flat into the ground while the first one is lifted. That is the fundamental idea; there are many variations; besides, the shoulders and head are made to synchronize or syncopate.

[13]I am not romancing nor translating loosely; *hay-dutsi-la* means literally "by thinking." The radical *hay–* means "Thought"; *dutsi* is the verb "to be" used here as an auxiliary in participal form (i.e. "being"); *-la* is the suffix representing the instrumental case (i.e. "by").

[14]Those big clumps of coarse grass and sod which gradually rise above the level of the water on the marshes are called *tsapettia*.

"Didn't they make people, too?"

"No. Not people. Not Indians.[15] The Indians came much later, after the world was spoiled by a crazy woman, Loon. But that's a long story. . . . I'll tell you some day."

"All right, Bill, but tell me just one thing now: there was a world now; then there were a lot of animals living on it, but there were no people then. . . ."

"Wha' d'you mean there were no people? Ain't animals people?"

"Yes, they are . . . but . . ."

"They are not Indians, but they are people, they are alive . . . Whad'you mean animal?"

"Well . . . how do you say 'animal' in Pit River?"

". . . I dunno. . . ."

"But suppose you wanted to say it?"

"Well . . . I guess I would say something like *teeqaade-wade toolol aakaadzi* (world-over, all living) . . . I guess that means animals, Doc."

"I don't see how, Bill. That means people, also. People are living, aren't they?"

"Sure they are! that's what I am telling you. Everything is living, even the rocks, even that bench you are sitting on. Somebody *made that bench for a purpose,* didn't he? Well then *it's alive,* isn't it? Everything is alive. That's what we Indians believe. White people think everything is dead. . . ."

"Listen, Bill. How do you say 'people'?"

"I don't know . . . just *is,* I guess."

"I thought that meant 'Indian.'"

"Say . . . Ain't we *people?!*"

"So are the whites!"

"Like hell they are!! We call them *inillaaduwi,* 'tramps,' nothing but tramps. They don't believe anything is alive. They are

---

[15]The word for "people" is *is.* Nowadays it is applied especially to Indians, in contradistinction to the term applied to the whites: *enellaaduwi.*

dead themselves. I don't call that 'people.' They are smart, but they don't know anything. . . . Say, it's getting late, Doc, I am getting sleepy. I guess I'll go out and sleep on top of the haystack. . . ."

"But you'll die of cold! It's already freezing, these nights."

"Naw, I won't. I am an Indian. I am used to it."

"But why don't you sleep here, inside?"

"WHAT?! Are you crazy? That woman might come and kill me."

"You mean Lena?"

"Shh! . . . Doc! For God's sake don't call her, don't call her name! Just say: the woman who died. That's bad enough. She is probably somewhere around, somewhere around here. They haven't burnt her things yet, you know, her baskets, her blankets, her clothes . . . all these things are calling her, are calling her shadow, her *de'lamdzi*."

"But why should she hurt you?"

"She don't want to hurt me."

"But you just said she might kill you. . . ."

"Well, she'll take my shadow away with her, and then I'll die."

"What for would she take your shadow away with her?"

"Oh, to keep from getting lonely on the road to the land of the dead people."

"Where is that?"

"I dunno. Nobody knows. Somewhere out west. They say there is a big lake there, no end to it, and the dead people live there on an island . . . I dunno . . . that's what I've heard."

"But, Bill, I still don't see why she should want to take you there. . . ."

"I just told you, Doc: to keep from getting lonely on the trip to the land of the dead. You would do the same thing yourself if you were going to a strange place. You would take along someone you knew and liked."

"Well then, she might take me, Bill. I know she liked me."

"Sure! That's why I tell you that you are a damn fool to sleep here!"

"Listen, Bill, tell me something else before you go . . . about the shadow, what do you call it, the *dalilamdzi?*"

"Naw, that means 'to make a shadow,' for instance *salilamdzi,* that means I am making a shadow, *kalilamdzi* it's you who are making a shadow. . . . No, Doc, I know what you are thinking about, that's the *de'lamdzi,* the shadow, that's not the same as *dalilamdzi,* that's the shadow . . . oh, hell, I dunno what's the difference, it kind of sounds the same, don't it? Lissen: I remember when I was a little boy I used to hear the old men when they woke in the morning, they used to sing:

dalilamdzi	*walilamdzi*	*de'lamdzi*	*seena seena*
(the dawn	is dawning	a shadow	I come home,
			I come home)

"So the *dalilamdzi,* that means the dawn, also! The old people they would hum like that when they woke up in the morning and they said: My shadow is liable to go wandering during the night and mebbe get lost and not find me again in the morning, that's why I sing to show him where I am! . . . Well, I think you are foolish to sleep here in this shack where she is liable to come back and take another look at her baskets that she made herself, and her stove, and everything, her shadow is, and it may ask your shadow to go along, and there will be no more Buckaroo Doc, and we will bury you and burn all your things, your saddle, and your book, and everything and everybody will cry . . . well, good night, Doc!"

Wild Bill stayed there several days, waiting for Jack Folsom and the other people to come back from the Hat Creek country where they had buried "the woman who had died." He was an excellent raconteur and told many old-time stories. There are tribes where the old-time stories and "myths" (as the anthropologists call them) are stereotyped, may even be cast in a rigid form and must be recited verbatim. But not so with the Pit

Rivers! A poor story-teller gives you the barest outline, in short sentences (nearly all beginning with "and then . . ."), in a monotonous voice. But a good raconteur like Wild Bill or old Mary tells it with gestures, mimicry, imitation noises—a regular theatrical performance. If there are several people in the audience, they grunt in approval after each telling passage. Instead of applauding by clapping as we do, they raise their chins and say: Hunh. . . .

Finally, one day about noon, Jack and all the relatives returned; five or six wagons full of them and immediately everything was confusion and pandemonium in this quiet corner of the sagebrush behind the little hill. They started a big bonfire. There was a lot of argument going on. Some of the people were still wailing. A woman would come dragging things out of the house, maybe two or three baskets, maybe an armful of clothes, and throw them into the fire; then she would go out a little way into the sagebrush and wail. The men were mostly silent and preoccupied; some of them wailed in man fashion: a sort of deep grunt, Honh-ho-ho, honh-ho-ho. . . . They carried things swiftly out of the house, threw them into the fire, and went back for more. Some of them were arguing (they wouldn't have been Pit Rivers if there hadn't been some kind of argument going on!); there was a little man who kept coming to me and complaining that they ought to burn the house, also. That seemed to be a moot point because in the old days there were no individual houses. And besides, according to Wild Bill, it was Jack's house, as well as the woman's who had died. . . . But the little old man was all for destruction. At least they should throw the stove into the fire. "But it won't burn!" said Wild Bill. "Well, throw it into the creek, then," said the fundamentalist.

I was sitting in my little tent, trying to keep out of the way. All this had happened so fast, like a whirlwind out of the sagebrush, that I was dazed. But everybody kept coming into my tent either to prove to me or to themselves that they were right, or to ask me if this or that object were mine, before throwing it into the fire. My copy of *Moby Dick* nearly went, and a horse's hackamore that belonged to me. Wild Bill stuck in my tent most of the time, sardonic as usual: "That's Indians for you! Just watch them, Doc. . . . Crazy goddam bunch. Always argue, always argue; argue all the time. . . . I wish they would get through with that burning. I have three colts I am breaking, at Tuluukupi, I left them in the corrals, I guess them fellows will feed them . . . still, I ought to be getting back to them."

Jack Folsom himself didn't seem to be doing anything except going around, wailing, crying, grunting. He came into my tent and sat on my cot and sobbed like a little child. "She was very good, that woman, Doc. She never quarreled. I have had four, no, five, before her. We have been together a long time now. You know my daughter Jessie, well she raised her. Jessie has got grandchildren now."

"But, Jack, I thought Jessie was this woman's daughter. . . ."

"No, another woman's. I have had three women already, no, four. No, two only, according to Indian way. This woman I paid for her and she paid for me. That's according to Indian law. I gave Jack Wilson, you know . . . the old fellow who was singing that night, I gave him a white mare, she was awful fast, she had won several races for me, and her people gave me the right to fish on Hat Creek. . . . But you noticed that woman that's come in with them? She is ordering everything around, she is bossing everybody. . . ."

"Yes, I noticed her. Who is she?"

"She is younger sister of the woman who died, what we call *enun,* same as what you call "cousin." So, she has come to claim me."

"What do you mean, claim you?"

"It's this way, Doc: according to Indian law, *the dead people have got the say;* the relations of the dead person have got the right. If I had died, then my people, my relations, they are the ones who have the right to bring another man in my place. It don't matter he is an old man good for nothing. They say: We bought that woman, she belongs to us now; here's a man for her; she take him, or give us back our present; we gave you a horse for her; where is that horse? Now, this woman who died, I married her according to Indian law. So, her people, her relations, they come here with this other woman, and they say to me: You lost one, here's another, you got no claim against us."

"Well, then, it's all right, isn't it?"

"No, it ain't all right, Doc. I don't want that woman. She is all right. She is young, I know. She is clean; she is a good worker . . . but she is bossy as hell! She'll boss me . . . I am too old to be bossed!"

Afterwards I took Jack down to my little ranch in the mountains south of Monterey. We had to go fifty miles by horse-stage, then fifteen miles more by trail over the ridges. When we were on top of the highest ridge the sun was dipping into the ocean, and we stopped to eat some sandwiches and make a little coffee. But before he ate, Jack chewed a piece and spat some to the east, and to the north, and to the south, and to the west. "See, Doc, I am doing that because I am in a new country. Them people you don't see, them coyotes and foxes and all kinds of *dinihowis* and *damaagomes* that live around here, they don't know me, because I am a stranger. They might hurt me. So I am telling them: I am all right, I don't mean no harm to you people, see, I am feeding you; and you people don't hurt me neither, because I am a stranger but I want to be friends with you. That's the way to do, Doc, that's the good way."

Night overtook us, and we went down the steep trail in the dark. Jack was stumbling. "Say, Doc, you sure picked you a darn steep country for your homestead." We reached the cabin at last, and I lit a fire in the hearth. There was an old rock mortar, of the kind the Indians use to pound acorns with a stone pestle. They still use them in Central California, but, for some reason which I don't understand, they don't use them any more in the Pit River country. Indeed, the Pit River Indians are afraid to touch them. "Them things are dangerous, Doc, them things are full of power. You come across one lying on the ground, some place; and the next day you'll find him mebbe a mile further away! He moved during the night!" Whether it was only the ones that were lying abandoned "some place," or whether it was *all* mortars, I never found out. Anyway, I never saw any in use among the Pit Rivers. And now, Jack was very much shocked because I had one of these mortars lying near the hearth! "You shouldn't do that, Doc! He is getting too hot there, near the fire . . . make him mad . . . he is liable to hurt you, bring you bad luck, maybe make your children sick. . . ."

But Jack did not stay very long at my little ranch. He was having bad dreams. "I been dreaming of blood, Doc. It's those people working against me, my wife's people, the one who died. They have got some powerful doctors on their side. I should have married that sister of hers when she came to claim me. That's Indian law. I can't get out of it!"

So I put him on the stage and he went back to Modoc and the joys of matrimony.

When I saw him the next summer he looked subdued. He greeted me with his usual warmth, but when I asked him how he was getting along with his quondam sister-in-law, he said: "Oh, it's hell, Doc, just hell. I don't draw a free breath of my own."

I saw him again the next summer. He was radiant. "I got rid of her, Doc. I was camped at Davis Creek, and her brother he come and see me, and he says: Jack, I wouldn't stay with that woman, if I were you. She is too damn bossy! . . . Well, Doc, that's all I wanted to hear. He was her elder brother, so he had the say. So I called my own boy, Millard, you know him, and I said: I am going—when that woman comes back to the camp, don't tell her where I am gone—you don't know nothing about it, *sabe!*"

A few years later I found her married to Sukmit, of all people! But she had found her mate. They were yelling at each other, while old Mary smiled on complacently. Old Mary had earned her rest.

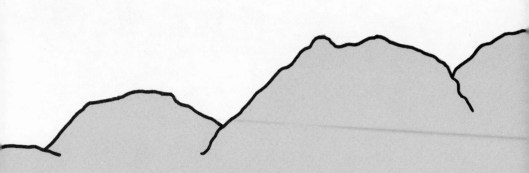

III: ON THE AUTHOR

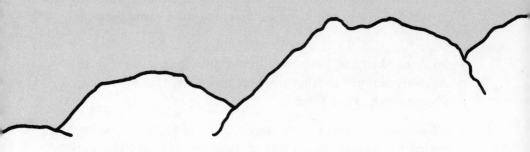

Jaime de Angulo:

an approximate chronology of the life and works.

1888 Born in Paris France where his family, engaged in a tax feud with the Spanish government, had taken up residence. Don Gregorio de Angulo, de Angulo's father, refuses to allow Spanish to be spoken in the home.

1900 Daily visits to the Musée Guimet. "A wonderful museum, filled with information on the mythologies of China, Japan, Tibet, Indo-China, Assyria, Babylonia, Egypt, Greece. Here I discovered to my great relief that not all religions were as flat, as absurd, as dead and boring as the Catholicism of my people. This was the beginning of my rebellion."

1904 Left for the Americas. Spent time (allegedly) as a prison guard in the British Honduras, and then entered the American West where he was employed as 'kowboy' on a cattle ranch in Wyoming.

1906 Arrived in San Francisco just in time for the great earthquake. Moved north to Alturas where he invested his life savings in a horse ranch in the Sierras.

1908 Decided to return, temporarily, to more formal schooling. Attended Cooper Medical College, then on to Johns Hopkins where he received a degree in Medicine. At Johns Hopkins met his first wife, Cary Fink, and both of them became active in the local Socialist Club. De Angulo's first know publication, *The Trial of Ferrer: A Clerical-Judicial Murder* published by the New York Labor Company in 1911.

1912-1915 Returned to California. Spent time both in Alturas, and in his new cabin home in Big Sur. Drove a herd of over five hundred horses down through the long, five hundred mile, central California valley, a fact which truly astonished his neighbors. First real contact with the Pit River Indians, many of whom will work for de Angulo on his horse ranch.

1915 World War One. De Angulo enters the Army Medical Corp, and is transferred to Ann Arbor Michigan as a faculty member where he will teach a course on modern psychology to his fellow officers.

1918 Back in California. Meets Paul Radin and Alfred Kroeber who invited JDA to put his growing knowledge of Indian Languages to use at the University of California, Berkeley. JDA also meets his soon-to-be second wife, L. F. Freeland (Nancy de Angulo).

1920 JDA's first 'Indian' essays begin to appear in *Laughing Horse*, a magazine edited by Spud Johnson, and published first out of Berkeley, and later from Taos. JDA meets D. H. Lawrence, and the two men 'most definitely' do not get along.

1922 JDA and Cary Fink divorced. That winter de Angulo writes *Don Bartolomeo*, his first novel which demonstrates both his debt and hostility to Lawrence.

1923 De Angulo moves to Berkeley where he marries Lucy (Nancy) Freeland, who is then a graduate student studying under Paul Radin. JDA hired to teach two courses at 'Cal': one on Jungian Psychology, the other on 'The Mind of Primitive Man'.

1924-1933 For the next twelve years, often in collaboration with Lucy Freeland, de Angulo will become one of the real linguistic 'hot-shots' in the West. Employed often by Doctor Franz Boas, de Angulo will master the fundamentals of seventeen distinct Native American Languages, often the most rare and obscure of such languages, as was Dr. Boas's special 'mission'. De Angulo, for example, will compose a *Shasta Dictionary and Grammar,* the first and last such effort as the last Shasta speaker will die within a few years. JDA's main area of concentration will become increasingly among the Native Peoples of Northern California.

1934 Meets Carl Jung, visiting in the American Southwest, and is employed by Jung as a translator. Those sections in Jung's later *Memories, Dreams and Reflections* with reference to conversations among the Pueblo were undoubtedly translated for Jung by de Angulo.

1935 De Angulo's home in Berkeley, built on land provided to him by the architect Bernard Maybeck, becomes the center of the local Bohemia. On any given weekend, or weekday for that matter, the house might be filled with visiting anthropologists, such as Malinowski or Sapir, de Angulo's Indian friends from the North, wandering Jazz musicians from over in Oakland, and assorted poets and artists from all about the area.

1936 De Angulo involved in a tragic car accident in Big Sur. His twelve-year-old son Alvar killed instantly, and de Angulo pinned in the car for over twelve hours before help arrives. De Angulo and his wife Nancy separate, she to stay on in Berkeley, he to move permanently to Big Sur.

1940 JDA becomes a central and legendary hermit figure in Big Sur, seen only with his friend Robinson Jeffers, or the musician Harry Partch. "The Three American Primitives". Henry Miller also becomes a sometime friend. 'Jaime de Angulo is the one man I regret never having written a book about', although Miller does provide a lengthy sketch in his book *The Devil in Paradise*.

1946 Still quite possibly 'clinically mad' de Angulo moves back to the Bay Area. He lives for awhile in Chinatown as a Drag Queen, and earns his living by giving language instruction to various students, including the young Jack Spicer.

1948 De Angulo known now to be dying of cancer. He returns to his home with Nancy in Berkeley, and concentrates for the most part on his writing. *Don Gregorio*, *The Lariat*, *Coyote's Bones*, *Indians in Overalls* and *Indian Tales* are all pulled into shape at this time. Poet Robert Duncan is hired as a live-in secretary to handle the typing chores.

1949 JDA reads *Indian Tales* to an 'astonished audience' over the local public broadcasting radio station, KPFA. *Indian Tales* becomes the most popular program in KPFA history, and is aired in the mornings twice a week.

1950 JDA in constant contact with Ezra Pound. Pound becomes JDA's unofficial 'stage manager' helping to place various pieces in different magazines. At Pound's urging Fred Morgan publishes *Indians in Overalls* in his *Hudson Review*, and a young Allen Ginsberg carries *Indian Tales* to his friend Carl Solomon, then editor at A. A. Wynn. Through Peter Russell in England Pound offers to edit a series of books to feature de Angulo's *The Lariat*, and works of W. Lewis—'the only two prose writers who can write more than a page at a time without putting EP to sleep.'

Four months after *Indians in Overalls* appears Jaime de Angulo dies of cancer. His body is cremated, and the ashes are scattered in the forests of Marin.

1954 *Indian Tales* published by A. A. Wynn.

1972-1977 The Turtle Island Foundation publishes the seven volume *Jaime de Angulo Library*, including *Coyote Man and Old Doctor Loon, Indians in Overalls, Don Bartolomeo, Coyote's Bones, The Lariat, Shabegok (Old Times Storeis, I.)* and *How the World was Made (Old Times Stories, II.)*. The series is designed and printed by Clifford Burke, and issued in a limited letter-press hardcover edition of a thousand each.

1979 First paperback publication of *A Jaime de Angulo Reader.*

This First Edition
designed by George Mattingly
with Matthew Carter's Galliard type
set by Graham Mackintosh
Autumn 1979